DEPARTMENT OF PHYSIOLOGY,

THE UNIVERSITY,

SHEFFIELD, 10

6/6.
1/4.

EXPERIMENTAL PHYSIOLOGY

EXPERIMENTAL PHYSIOLOGY

BY

GEORGE H. BELL, B.Sc., M.D.

Muirhead Lecturer in Physiology
University of Glasgow

THIRD EDITION

JOHN SMITH & SON (GLASGOW) LTD.
26-30 GIBSON STREET, HILLHEAD
GLASGOW, W. 2
1944

Printed in Great Britain by J. & J. Gray, Edinburgh

CONTENTS

PREFACE TO FIRST EDITION

THE present small practical book has been devised to suit the needs of the experimental course in Physiology for medical students at Glasgow University. In the selection of work to be done an attempt has been made to assemble practical material which, while illustrating the fundamental principles, would at the same time have a direct bearing on the future work of the student. Experience in teaching has shown that the course does give satisfactory results in spite of the handicaps of large classes and limited laboratory time. No claim for originality is made for the experiments described; indeed, many of them are quite ancient—Scheiner's and Harvey's being several hundred years old.

The practical work is supplemented by demonstrations of the activities of mammalian preparations, electro-cardiograph, etc., but no account of these demonstrations is included.

It will be noted that very little explanation of results is given. The student is expected to make up his own mind about the conclusions to be drawn from his experimental results and to consult his text-book for further details.

The course of practical work described here is a modification of that first drafted by my predecessor, Dr. R. C. Garry.

I am very grateful to Professor Cathcart for his careful reading of the manuscript and for much valuable advice. I have to thank my colleagues in this department for help in settling various points, also the publishers and printers for the excellent way in which they have carried out their work.

G. H. B.

INSTITUTE OF PHYSIOLOGY,
   THE UNIVERSITY,
      GLASGOW.
December 1936.

PREFACE TO SECOND EDITION

THIS edition is larger than its predecessor because of the longer time now given to experimental physiology. The programme arrangement of the first edition has been altered to a systematic arrangement of experiments, but a plan of our junior course is included.

By the generous co-operation of Professor McDowall and Professor Garry I have been able to include experiments from their courses at King's College, London, and University College, Dundee, which are not contained in the Glasgow scheme.

I am indebted to Professor Cathcart for his careful reading of the manuscript, and I have benefited once more from the advice of my colleagues. The publishers and printers have maintained their high standard.

G. H. B.

INSTITUTE OF PHYSIOLOGY,
   THE UNIVERSITY,
      GLASGOW.
September 1940.

PREFACE TO THIRD EDITION

WAR-TIME conditions have permitted only a few minor alterations and additions to this edition.

G. H. B.

INSTITUTE OF PHYSIOLOGY,
   THE UNIVERSITY,
      GLASGOW.
October 1943.

PROGRAMME OF JUNIOR EXPERIMENTAL COURSE AT GLASGOW UNIVERSITY

The numbers refer to the sections numbered in bold type in brackets

Meetings One and Two
Benches 1 and 2 (Two Hours), **10, 11, 12**
Benches 3 and 4 (Two Hours), **1**

Meetings Three and Four
Benches 1 and 2 (Two Hours), **13, 14, 20**
Benches 3 and 4 (Two Hours), **3, 4, 5, 6**

Meetings Five and Six
Bench 1 (One Hour), **22, 23,** and **16, 18, 24**
Bench 2 (One Hour), **7**
Benches 3 and 4 (Two Hours), **8**

Meeting Seven
All Benches (Two Hours), **28, 29, 30**

Meeting Eight
Half an Hour at each Bench
Bench 1, **36, 37, 38, 39**
Bench 2, **40, 41, 49**
Bench 3, **42, 43**
Bench 4, **44, 45, 46, 47, 48**

Meeting Nine
Half an Hour at each Bench
Bench 1, **56**
Bench 2, **59, 60, 61, 62, 63, 64, 65**
Bench 3, **50, 51, 52, 53, 54, 55**
Bench 4, **58, 57**

Meeting Ten
Half an Hour at each Bench
Bench 1, **66, 67** (1) and (2)
Bench 2, **74, 70, 71, 73**
Bench 3, **75** (1), (2) and (3)
Bench 4, **76**

8

Meeting Eleven
Half an Hour at each Bench
Bench 1, **96, 97, 98, 99**
Bench 2, **79, 80, 85, 86, 87, 89**
Bench 3, **82**
Bench 4, **72, 90, 88, 77, 81**

Meeting Twelve
Bench 1 (Half an Hour), **91, 92, 93, 94, 95**
Bench 2 (Half an Hour), **83, 84, 69, 78, 68**
Benches 3 and 4 (One Hour), **31, 32, 33, 110**

Meeting Thirteen
Benches 1 and 2 (One Hour), **121, 120, 119, 124**
Benches 3 and 4 (One Hour), **9, 34**

Meeting Fourteen
Bench 1 (Half an Hour), **111, 112**
Bench 2 (Half an Hour), **100, 115, 114**
Benches 3 and 4 (One Hour), **122, 123, 116**

Meeting Fifteen
Benches 1 and 2 (One Hour), **104, 105**
Benches 3 and 4 (One Hour), **102, 103, 106, 101, 113**

Meeting Sixteen
Benches 1 and 2 (One Hour), **137**
Benches 3 and 4 (One Hour), **138**

Meeting Seventeen
Benches 1 and 2 (One Hour), **125, 34, 108 §1, 140**
Benches 3 and 4 (One Hour), Revision

INTRODUCTION

In the experimental course the activities of living tissues are examined. Many tissues can be activated very conveniently by electrical stimulation, and the resulting movement can be recorded on rotating drums.

Arrangement of Laboratory.

The arrangement of terminals on the bench applies to the Institute of Physiology, Glasgow. In other laboratories different arrangements will be found. A space is left here so that the student can insert the local interpretation of C, I, and T terminals. If a switch is not included in the terminal board on the bench a single pole switch should be added to all the circuits given here. As experimental physiological apparatus is by no means standard other local variations may be found. They may be entered here or in the text.

In the experimental laboratory each of the four benches has a shaft running along its midline driven by a motor under the bench. The shaft carries pulleys for driving the kymographs and also the interrupter discs described below. At each place there is a drawer for small articles, viz. connecting flex, blotting-paper, pin electrodes, and also a cupboard for kymograph drum, induction coil, switches, etc. At the end of each lesson all pieces of apparatus will be returned to their appropriate places.

In front of the shafting there is a switchboard with terminals.

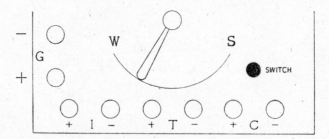

The C terminals give continuous current from a 4-volt accumulator. The T terminals give time impulses. See Time-marking. The I terminals give interrupted current for the induction coil.

See Induction Coil. The I terminals are connected to the 4-volt accumulator through the interrupter disc on the shafting. This consists of a fibre disc with copper segments on which bear four copper brushes. When the I terminals are not required the brushes are held back by a catch to avoid unnecessary wear. When a segment comes under a copper brush then current can flow through any apparatus (e.g. the primary coil of the induction coil) connected to the I terminals. The speed of the shafting and the number of brushes is such that the current is "made" and "broken" about forty times per second.

The switch (just behind the C terminals) controls the current from both C and I terminals; for some experiments it is used as a hand-manipulated interrupter. When the switch is "down" current is cut off from C and I terminals; always put the switch down when current is not required. G terminals are provided only on Bench 1 (nearest the entrance door). The output from these terminals is controlled by a potentiometer of approximately 50 ohms. The finger of the potentiometer is moved by the handle from W to S (weak to strong). The potentiometer has 16 volts across it. The G terminals are used when a steady current is required for stimulating tissues.

Care should be taken when connecting wires to the terminals to see that adjacent terminals are not short-circuited by frayed ends of wire; metal instruments should not be laid between the terminals. A short is the most usual cause of failure of electrical apparatus; if this does not explain a failure trace out the circuit from one terminal on the switchboard back to the other one.

Galvanic and Faradic.

Be it noted here that the terms "galvanic" and "faradic" should be abolished. The former must be in any case further specified—e.g. a potential of 1 volt was applied for one second to the tissue. A "faradic" current is an induced current produced by an induction coil. Its special peculiarity is that it lasts for a very short time, whereas a "galvanic" current is a steady current (from a battery) which may last a very long time. The peak or maximum voltage used in "faradic" stimulation may be of any order, but it is usually greater than that employed in "galvanic" stimulation. "Faradisation" means that the tissue is stimulated by a rapid series of induced currents. These remarks may help

the student better to understand text-books which are inclined to give the idea that these two currents are mysteriously different.

Induction Coil.

For students' purposes the induction coil is the best apparatus for producing brief electrical impulses. It consists of a primary coil wound with fairly thick copper wire over a bundle of soft iron wires. This coil is fixed to the baseboard of the instrument, and the copper wire ends at two terminals on the top of the vertical piece of wood supporting the coil. The secondary coil consists of a very large number of turns of fine copper wire ending at two terminals carried on the horizontal wood base supporting this coil, which can be slid nearer to or farther away from the primary coil. The distance between the two coils can be read at the pointer attached to the base of the secondary coil which travels over a centimetre scale fixed to the base of the instrument.

Any change of current in the primary coil will induce a current in the secondary coil. If the current is flowing steadily, or is zero, in the primary coil then there will be no current induced in the secondary circuit. The strength of the induced current varies inversely as the distance between the coils (being strongest when the secondary is right over the primary) and is greater the more sudden the alteration of the current in the primary coil. When the primary current is switched on (i.e. "made") it takes some time to grow to its maximum value owing to the inductance of the primary coil. This is characteristic of any coil—any change in the current flowing in it is opposed. When the primary current is switched off (i.e. "broken") then it falls to zero very suddenly. The induced current at "break" is, therefore, greater than the induced current at "make."

To obtain a rapid succession of these "make" and "break" currents (often loosely called "shocks") connect the primary coil to the I terminals and let the copper brushes down on the interrupter disc. (This replaces the Neef's hammer or electric bell trembling movement which, although usually fitted, is in many ways unsatisfactory. If I terminals are not available, the demonstrator will indicate the terminals to use to bring Neef's hammer into use.) The C terminals are used when the experimenter requires a single stimulus or a series of stimuli slower than that supplied by the I terminals, e.g. when the drum, tetanus

B

spring, or other form of interrupter is used to make and break the primary circuit.

Some of the coils are provided with small metal rectifiers: these are marked with a large R. The "make current" flows in the secondary coil in the opposite direction to the "break current" and can therefore be prevented from flowing by means of a rectifier or a valve connected in the secondary circuit in the appropriate direction. The elimination of the "make shock" will be found very useful in many experiments. Note very carefully that in the case of the coils with the rectifiers the primary terminals are marked + and −, and that these must be connected to the C or I terminals + to + and − to −. To avoid damage to the rectifiers the primary and secondary coils should not be moved any nearer to one another than is necessary to obtain a satisfactory muscle twitch. In other words have the coils as far apart as possible consistent with satisfactory stimulation.

The secondary terminals must always be connected to a friction switch, so that the secondary coil is shorted when the switch is closed. The pin electrodes used for stimulating the tissue are also connected across the switch so that current can pass through them across the tissue only when the switch is opened. This prevents polarisation in the tissue.

Kymograph.

The kymograph, or more simply the drum, consists of a gear-box with a vertical spindle carrying a 6-inch diameter drum. At the side of the gear-box is a cone of pulleys. A loop of string is passed over a pulley on the shafting and over a pulley on the drum. As the drums vary in type the actual positions of levers, etc., will be demonstrated in the laboratory. Each has a clutch lever for starting and stopping, and another lever with three positions : fast, neutral, and slow. By utilising the various sizes of pulleys on the shafting and on the kymograph, plus the large reduction gear brought into action at the "slow" position, a very large range of speeds of the periphery of the drum can be obtained. For example, to make the drum travel as fast as possible use the largest pulley on the shafting and the smallest on the drum with the lever in the fast gear position; to make the drum travel as slowly as possible use the smallest pulley on the shafting and the largest on the drum with the lever in the "slow" position.

At the base of the vertical spindle carrying the drum are two

projecting arms which can be moved stiffly on the spindle. When the drum is rotated these arms come into contact with an insulated spring contact on the side or on the base of the drum. The arms and the spring contact are connected to terminals so that electrical impulses may be sent into a tissue at prearranged times.

When making records the drum should revolve in a clockwise direction.

Smoking.

Moisten the gummed edge of the kymograph paper. Holding the gummed edge in the left hand wrap the paper glossy side out round the drum. When it is all square and tight press down the gummed edge, which should overlap from left to right.

If a fume cupboard is available smoke the drum in it to keep the laboratory clean. Coal gas is passed through a can packed with pumice soaked in benzene. This gives a very sooty flame when a fish-tail burner is used. Set the drum revolving at its fastest speed and bring the flame slowly and steadily down the drum; only the yellow part of the flame should be in contact with the paper. The layer of soot should be a dull black-brown, and not too thick. Mark the position of the overlap by rubbing off some soot near the top.

Time-marking.

All work with rotating drums really records graphically the relation—movement of organ against time. The ordinate, movement, is easily measured at any time, but the abscissa, time, must have its value recorded during the time of experiment. No traceing is of any value unless it carries a time-trace.

Where the drum is moving rapidly a trace is made by a tuning-fork of frequency 100 cycles per second. Hold the stem of the fork in the right hand and strike it *on the left palm,* then press the vibrating end with the writing point lightly against the drum. The flat surfaces of the blades must be kept in a horizontal plane. The right hand can be steadied by supporting it in the palm of the left hand, the left elbow resting on the bench.

The T terminals on the bench are connected to an electric clock which momentarily connects the terminals to a battery (12 volts) every 1 second or 10 seconds or 60 seconds. The interval required for each bench can be selected by plug contacts in a case on the laboratory wall. An electromagnetic marker connected to

these terminals is allowed to write gently against the drum. This time-recording is suitable for experiments requiring a slowly revolving drum as, for example, in heart experiments.

Tracings.

To remove the paper from the drum cut through it at any convenient part (usually near the overlapped join) by inserting a closed forceps (or a knife with its back to the drum) behind the upper edge of the paper. Push the forceps or knife down while holding the paper in position. *Never use a knife with the blade towards the drum, i.e. cutting on the metal surface of the drum.*

Lay the paper flat on the table and, using a hand-rest, write on any annotations necessary for the explanation of the curves— e.g. *MOMENT OF STIMULATION, TIME IN SECONDS, DISTANCE IN CENTIMETRES BETWEEN PRIMARY AND SECONDARY COILS.* Put your *NAME* on the trace, with the *DATE,* and varnish it by pulling the paper *slowly* once through a pool of varnish or over the varnishing-drum. *Allow excess varnish to drip back into the tray.* The trace is then pinned to the drying-rack near the fan and should be dry in less than half an hour. The drying can be hastened if the trace is laid on the metal cover over the radiators after drying for five minutes on the rack. All traces, if dry, should be collected before leaving the laboratory. If not, they will be found at the next meeting on the shelf labelled Section A, B, C, and D. The varnish is a solution of colophony resin in methylated spirits, with a small quantity of castor oil or liquid paraffin to prevent the varnish from setting too hard.

Trim the traces in the guillotine, and paste or gum them into your book. When working in pairs or fours a tracing should be obtained for each student. An ink or pencil copy of a trace will not be accepted unless in the one or two experiments in which it is impossible to obtain duplicates.

Laboratory Records.

This book is provided with blank pages for the keeping of records of experiments. When completed it will provide the student with a compact book of reference, and it will enable the teacher to discover whether the work has been conscientiously carried out.

Write in your remarks as near as possible to the printed description of the method. Under the heading RESULTS should be

given traces, diagrams, graphs and any calculation; traces and graphs should be carefully labelled so that no further description is required. A very brief description may be required of human experimental work. Under the heading Conclusions an attempt should be made to answer the question under investigation. Elaborate conclusions cannot be drawn from one experiment: do not give as your deduction a mere restatement of the results.

Write very briefly and then you will have time to write legibly. Bad writing is an affectation which is heartily to be condemned; it is often merely a cloak for ignorance.

Solutions to be used in Contact with Living Tissues.

Cells are harmed or killed if placed in pure water; special solutions must be used to keep exposed tissues moist or to perfuse or bathe surviving organs.

Ringer's solution for frog work.—The composition of this fluid is: NaCl 0·6%, KCl 0·0075%, $NaHCO_3$ 0·01%, $CaCl_2$ 0·01%. This solution, when made up in glass distilled water, has been found by repeated trial to be a suitable medium for perfusion of frog tissues. It has the same osmotic pressure as the blood of the frog and is slightly alkaline. Also there is such a balance between the Ca and the K ions that the frog heart in this medium continues to beat for a very long time.

Locke's solution for mammalian work.—Tyrode's modification: NaCl 0·8%, KCl 0·02%, $NaHCO_3$ 0·1%, $MgCl_2$ 0·01%, NaH_2PO_4 0·005%, $CaCl_2$ 0·02%, Glucose 0·1%. This solution must also be made up in glass distilled water. As with frog Ringer all the constituents, with the exception of the $CaCl_2$, should be dissolved in almost the final volume; then the $CaCl_2$ is added and the volume made up to 100 per cent. This solution will not keep since it contains glucose. The omission of glucose will in many instances make no appreciable difference to the experimental results.

Fluid of this or similar composition is often given intravenously in man where there has been fluid loss. Tyrode leaves the blood vessels rather quickly, but this is delayed if 6 per cent. gum arabic is added. What is the reason for this?

CHAPTER ONE

SKELETAL MUSCLE AND NERVE

Preparation of Frog Material.

Note.—Each student must provide himself with a strong pair of scissors, a small pair which should cut right to the point, and two pairs of forceps, one fine. At the end of a day's use they should be washed in hot water, dried thoroughly, and rubbed over with a trace of vaseline.

The drum must be smoked and all apparatus got ready before obtaining any biological material.

The frog is held by the hind feet ventral surface uppermost and killed by swinging it smartly against the edge of the table.

Removal of the Hemispheres.—In some experiments it is necessary to remove the hemispheres only. Insert a scissors blade into the mouth and cut off the head just behind the eyes.

Decerebration.—Insert one blade of the scissors into the mouth and cut off the skull behind the tympanic membranes. If it is necessary to avoid excessive bleeding these operations can be carried out by crushing the brain between the blades of a Spencer Wells forceps.

Pithing.—Push a large pin down the vertebral canal; by rotary and side-to-side movements destroy the cord.

To avoid unnecessary waste it is usual to divide the frog into two parts. Hold the pithed (or in some cases decerebrated) frog belly upwards. It will be found that if the legs are held up vertically in the left hand then the body will fall over the index finger dorsal surface to dorsal surface of finger. Make a snip into the abdomen with the scissors and enlarge the opening laterally on both sides. Then cut across the body with scissors just a little nearer the head than the apex of the bend. The upper part is used for experimental work on the heart and the lower preparation is used for nerve and muscle experiments.

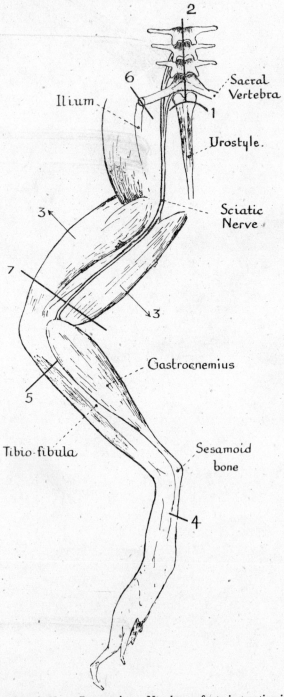

Illustration to Muscle-Nerve Preparation.   Numbers refer to instruction in text, p. 30.

Muscle-nerve Preparation.

During the preparation of any frog material keep the tissues, especially nerves, moist with frog Ringer. Use scissors, not a knife. Do not put any strain on a nerve; do not use forceps to grasp a nerve. Take the lower preparation just described and hold the stump of the vertebral column in one hand and grasp the dorsal skin between the folds of a cloth in the other hand. The trouser of skin can then readily be pulled off. Still holding the stump of the vertebral column dorsal side up, cut out the urostyle (the cartilaginous prolongation of the vertebral column) with scissors (cut 1 in illustration). Keep the blades close to the urostyle. Push one scissors blade between the two diverging bundles of nerves to the legs, and divide the vertebral column into two halves (2 in illustration). Grasp the thigh dorsal side upwards between the fingers in such a way as to push apart the flexors and extensors (3) —the sciatic nerve will be at once apparent. A glass rod with a small rounded point dipped in saline is used to pull the muscles away from the nerve, which should be cleared from the spinal cord to the knee joint. Pass the glass rod between the tibio-fibula and the gastrocnemius muscle, and separate these from the knee joint to the sesamoid bone. Cut through the plantar insertion of the gastrocnemius distal to the sesamoid bone (4). Cut through the tibio-fibula (and the anterior tibial muscles) as near the knee as possible (5). Cut through the iliosacral joint (6), and bring the small piece of vertebral column with the attached sciatic nerve down over the gastrocnemius. Cut the femur as near the knee as possible, avoiding the sciatic nerve (7). Put the muscle-nerve preparation in Ringer solution.

In the following experiments the sciatic nerve is often exposed to the air and, therefore, it may easily dry. If the muscle after a period of quiescence suddenly shows spontaneous movements, this is not usually due to drying of the muscle, which has a comparatively large bulk, but to drying of the nerve, which has a very large surface relative to its bulk. The nerve can be kept moist by pouring Ringer solution over it frequently. In the intervals of an experiment it is wise to take the nerve off the pin electrodes, lay it on the muscle, and cover both with a small piece of blotting-paper and pour Ringer solution over it.

Simple Muscle Twitch.

(1) To record the course of contraction. Apparatus required:

drum, induction coil, muscle lever, pillar on adjustable base, frog board, pin electrodes, wires. Set up all apparatus and smoke the drum before obtaining frog material. Circuit is as follows (see diagram): one C terminal (accumulator) to primary coil, primary coil to drum terminal, other drum terminal back to C (accumulator); secondary coil short-circuited by switch, pin electrodes across switch. Clamp the frog board on the adjustable pillar and

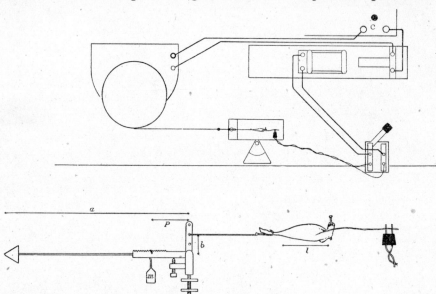

cover the cork with paraffin waxed paper to prevent contamination of the muscle and nerve by salts, drugs, etc., previously soaked into the cork. Lay the muscle-nerve preparation on blotting-paper, soaked in Ringer, placed on the waxed paper. Put the muscle lever into the slot provided on the frog board and clamp it in position about half way along the slot. Place a 5-gm. weight (or more in the case of a large muscle) on the serrated edge of the muscle lever about 2 cm. from the fulcrum. Pick up the bent pin attached by a thread to the short arm of the muscle lever and push it through the tendon of the gastrocnemius proximal to the sesamoid bone (i.e. between the bone embedded in the tendon and the muscle). Pull the tendon gently into the crook of the pin. Push a straight pin into the cavity of the femur and on till it emerges from the femur. Pull gently on this pin to make the long arm of the muscle lever horizontal and push the pin firmly into the c

frog board to maintain this position. Take care that the bent pin is clear of the blotting-paper. The weight of the lever will now be borne by the muscle. Screw up the afterloading screw (a little screw near and below the fulcrum of the lever) until the weight is just taken off the muscle. This ensures an even base line. Lay the nerve across the pin electrodes, which are fastened by a pin to the frog board. Keep the nerve moist with Ringer, but do not allow a large drop to gather between the electrodes as this will short-circuit the nerve.

Turn round the drum until one of the contact arms touches the electric contact on the base of the drum. Move the switch on the terminal board up and down (the circuit is broken when the switch moves down) with the short-circuiting switch open and move the secondary coil in or out (starting at about 30 cm.) until the muscle contracts at "break" only (see Induction Coil, p. 16). The point of the writing lever should be adjusted to move in a plane parallel to the surface of the drum, and the lever should be at right angles to the radius of the drum at the point of contact (i.e. tangential). Set the drum contact arms at 180° apart, making one of them point to the junction of the smoked paper. Close the shorting switch in the secondary circuit. Keep the lever just off the smoked paper. Start the drum revolving at nearly the fastest speed (largest pulley on shafting to second smallest on drum). Pull up the switch on the terminal board, open the shorting switch and note the twitches. This phantom trace will demonstrate whether or not all is in order. If the contacts were adjusted as suggested then the records will not fall on the junction of the smoked paper.

Close the shorting switch. Push the lever lightly against the drum about one inch above the lower edge by rotating the movable base-piece of the pillar. When the drum is rotating steadily open the shorting switch—two twitches will occur—close the switch quickly. *Leave everything* as it is. Stop the drum with the clutch lever. To mark the moment of stimulation revolve the drum slowly by hand in the same direction as before, keeping the switch in the secondary circuit closed till the striker is just about to make contact, then open the switch; very cautiously and steadily continue the movement of the drum till the muscle contracts at "break" and so marks the moment of stimulation with a vertical line. Project the apex of the curve down to the base line, by moving the lever with the finger at the correct

position. Repeat for the other trace which is 180° from the first. Run a time-trace with the tuning-fork. Keep the preparation, especially the nerve, moist with Ringer so that it will be in good condition for further experiments.

Measure: latent period, contraction period, relaxation period, also length of muscle, dimensions of lever and position of weight.

Calculate: actual shortening of muscle, mass lifted by muscle, work done by muscle.

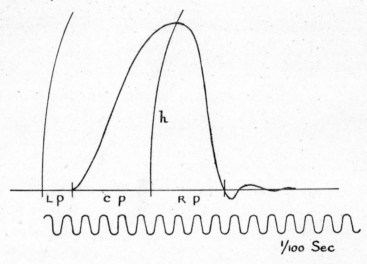

The actual shortening of the muscle, x, is h divided by the magnification of the lever, $x = \dfrac{hb}{a}$ cms. If the mass lifted is y, then $yb = pm$ so $y = \dfrac{pm}{b}$ gms. Thus the weight lifted is $\dfrac{pm}{b} \cdot g$ dynes. The work done is therefore $\dfrac{pmg}{b} \cdot \dfrac{hb}{a} = \dfrac{pmgh}{a}$ ergs.

(For the meaning of a, b, h, m, p, see the two diagrams given above. For explanation of calculations see physics text-book.)

Isometric Contraction.

(2) In the previous experiment the load on the muscle was constant—i.e. isotonic. If an isometric lever is substituted for the isotonic one, then an isometric contraction can be recorded by precisely the same technique. It will be seen that the lever is attached to a wire which can twist very slightly. Tie a strong

thread round the tendon and tie it to the lever near the fulcrum. The knee joint is held firmly in a clamp placed above the lever and adjusted so that the muscle is stretched slightly. Proceed exactly as with the isotonic lever.

Effect of Load and Length on Muscle.

(3) The apparatus required is exactly as in the simple muscle twitch experiment (p. 30). Wire up the induction coil to C terminals (4-volt accumulator) but do not include the drum in the circuit. Smoke the drum and get the muscle-nerve preparation ready. Arrange the muscle on the frog board so that the lever is

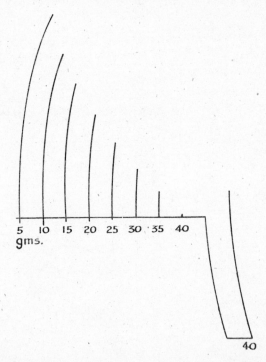

horizontal and just supported by the after-loading screw with no weight on the lever. The muscle will thus not have the weight applied to it till after it begins to contract—i.e. it is afterloaded. By moving the switch on the terminal board up and down, find a break shock which is sufficient to give an adequate contraction of the muscle. Bring the writing point lightly against the drum and about half way down it. Take a record—a single line—of the

contraction of the unloaded muscle on the stationary drum. Move round the drum about 0·5 cm. by hand. Place a 5-gm. weight on the serrated edge of the muscle lever. Record the contraction, again move round the drum about 0·5 cm. Continue to add weights, advancing by 5 gm. on each occasion, and always placing the weight on the serrated edge of the lever at the same place. Take records until a weight is found which the muscle is just unable to lift. Then move the drum on 0·5 cm., lower the afterloading screw and allow the muscle to be stretched by this heavy weight without support from the screw. The muscle is thus loaded at rest. Move the drum along another 0·5 cm. Stimulate the nerve again—the muscle will contract and raise the weight. Remove all weights. Keep the muscle-nerve preparation moist with Ringer solution. Label the tracing with the weights used.

Calculate the work done at each twitch and graph work (ordinate) against load (abscissa). Draw conclusions as to optimum conditions for muscle work.

The Effect of Strength of Stimulus.

(4) Connections as for load and length above. Lever gently touching the drum. 5-gm. weight on lever. Take the secondary coil well away from the primary—breaking the primary circuit will

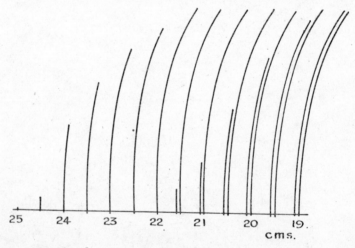

not now stimulate the nerve and cause the muscle to contract. Gradually diminish the distance between primary and secondary coils until a "break" shock causes a small contraction. Move the

secondary coil 0·5 cm. nearer, move the drum 0·5 cm. round by hand, break the primary circuit. Repeat until the maximum height of contraction is obtained. Before this, however, the "make" shocks may have become effective; the resulting contractions should be recorded about 1 mm. in front of "break."

Explain these findings partly on physical grounds and partly on "all or none" law. Note that with induction coils provided with rectifiers the secondary coil may need to be pushed very near before "make" twitches appear. Read Induction Coil in the introduction, p. 16.

Effect of Temperature on the Course of Muscular Contraction.

(5) Put the drum contacts in the primary circuit. Speed—second fastest possible. Take two twitches (180° apart) as described before (p. 30). Swing the writing point off the drum, pour Ringer at 0° C. over the muscle. Replace the lever on the drum and take another tracing (i.e. two twitches) on top of the previous tracing as soon as possible. Swing the lever off and pour Ringer at 30° C. over the muscle; record other two twitches on top of the previous. Compare the forms of the three twitches which have the same moment of stimulation.

Effect of Prolonged Exercise (Fatigue).

(6) Connect the drum in the primary circuit as before. Find a position of the secondary coil which gives a "break" shock sufficient to produce a good contraction of the muscle, but which gives an ineffective "make" shock. (This condition is easily attained with coils with rectifiers.) Slack off the clamping screw; but keep the slot of the triangular base-piece of the pillar hard against the clamping screw and move the whole frog board and stand till the point of the lever is writing on the drum. Record two twitches (180° apart) on the third fastest speed. Mark the moments of stimulation. Open the shorting switch again and swing the lever off the drum; start up the drum once more and count twitches "3, 4, . . . 19, 20." Swing the lever smartly back into position so that the end of the slot is touching the clamping screw and record 21, 22; swing off, count "23 . . . 40." Record 41, 42, and so on until fatigue is quite marked. In fresh preparations it may be better to record 1, 2; 51, 52; 101, 102, etc. When the muscle-nerve preparation is completely fatigued stick the pin electrodes into the muscle and stimulate again. Cut across the

muscle with scissors and test the reaction of the muscle with litmus paper. Draw deductions concerning latent period, contraction period, relaxation period, amplitude of contraction. Read about chemical and other changes in muscle in fatigue.

Rate of Passage of the Nervous Impulse.

(7) The nerve is stimulated at a point close to the muscle, and then at a point as far away from it as possible. The latent period of the muscular contraction (i.e. the time elapsing from the stimulation of the muscle itself till the beginning of the rise of the lever) is the same in both cases; therefore any difference in the time elapsing between the moment of stimulation and the rise of the lever in the two cases will be due to the time taken for the nervous impulse to pass down the nerve between the points stimulated.

Put the drum contacts in the primary circuit of the induction coil; use C terminals (i.e. 4-volt accumulator). Place one pair of pin electrodes on the nerve as near the muscle as possible, put another pair as near the stump of the cord as possible; connect one pair to the short-circuiting switch. Find a "break" induced current which is sufficiently strong to produce a good contraction of the muscle. If it is not easy to do this without a contraction at "make" appearing, then use a "make" shock which produces a good contraction. (This difficulty will not arise with coils provided with rectifiers.) The double humped curve obtained by the quick succession of "make" and "break" shocks is no disadvantage in this experiment, as we are interested only in the beginning of the curve and not in its entire course.

Put the strikers on the drum 180° apart. Take two records (also 180° apart), on the fastest possible drum, of the course of contraction of the muscle. Without making any other alteration immediately connect the other pair of pin electrodes to the shorting switch and take another two records. If a two-pole change over switch is available then the centre pair of contacts should be connected to the shorting switch and a pair of pin electrodes connected to each of the outer pairs of contacts. The second record will be superimposed on the first. Mark the moment of stimulation on each record. Run a time-trace with the tuning-fork. Measure the length of the nerve between the two pairs of pin electrodes.

When the tracing is fixed measure the distance between two curves which have the same moment of stimulation, express this

in σ (sigma, thousandths of a second). Calculate the velocity of the nervous impulse in metres per second.

Genesis of Tetanus.

(8) Arrange the coil and drum for recording the course of contraction. Put the secondary coil at such a distance that the muscle contracts at "break" only. Bring the contact arms at the foot of the vertical drum spindle to an angle of about 45°. Record the two contractions near the lower edge of the drum. Bring the contact arms nearer so that the second stimulus falls on the relaxation period, and in the next experiment on the contraction period, of the first twitch. Take two records of each. Lower the drum after each tracing is made so that three separate graphs are obtained.

Remove the wires from the drum terminals and connect them to the mercury pool and to the terminal on the tetanus spring. Set the spring in its clamp to mark 4, so that when the spring is set vibrating (with the finger) the amalgamated wire at its end dips in and out of the mercury pool four times per second. Record the effect of a series of "break" stimuli at this rate on the fastest drum on the *low* gear. Set the spring vibrating, open the short-circuiting switch, close it when about 2 in. of paper have been covered. Repeat this to get a tracing for each student. Set the spring vibrating at 8 per sec., then at 16 per sec., and record as before. Then finally—after disconnecting the tetanus spring—change from C to I terminals, which give about 40 per sec. (or Neef's hammer), and record the effect on the same drum.

Human Muscle Twitch.

(9) The human ulnar nerve and flexor minimi digiti proprius make a "preparation" very like the frog muscle-nerve preparation. Prepare the apparatus as for the frog muscle experiments, and follow the technique given there with the following modifications. Clamp the special human muscle lever on the pillar instead of the frog board. Clamp the base of the pillar to keep everything as rigid as possible. Tie a weight (50–100 gm.) to the lever. Attach one end of a long piece of cotton thread to the lever at the hole farthest from the fulcrum, carry it over the pulley, then pass the subject's right little finger through a loop in the other end of the cotton. The bare forearm and wrist are supported on a wooden platform carrying a metal plate, covered with a cloth soaked in saline. The plate is connected by a flex wire to one side

of the shorting switch and forms an indifferent electrode. The arm should be held in a position midway between supination and pronation. It may be necessary for the experimenter to hold down the subject's wrist to prevent the action of the flexor carpi ulnaris. A small electrode covered with chamois leather soaked in saline is connected to the other side of the shorting switch. It is placed by the experimenter over the ulnar nerve as it passes over the groove on the posterior surface of the medial epicondyle of the humerus. The subject holds this electrode in position with the left hand. The current density below this electrode will be greater than below the larger one. The smaller will, therefore, be the stimulating electrode. When a record is obtained mark the moment of stimulation as before. Run a time-trace.

If you have a poor record of any frog muscle experiment, repeat with this "preparation."

D

CHAPTER TWO

CIRCULATION IN THE FROG

Recording of the Cardiac Cycle in the Frog.

APPARATUS required: frog board, pillar on adjustable base, frog heart lever, drum, needle and cotton thread. Study the anatomy of the heart as demonstrated by large plasticine models. Have all the apparatus ready and the drum smoked before beginning the experiment.

The frog is killed and divided into an upper and a lower portion as described on p. 26.

(**10**) Pin the upper part down on the frog board ventral side up. Pick up the abdominal wall with forceps and cut in the mid line

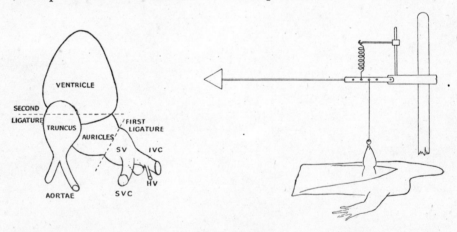

till the sternum is reached. Pick up the sternum with forceps, cut on either side with scissors, keeping the points well up and pointing slightly laterally. Cut through the shoulder girdle and cut through the base of the flap containing the sternum. Moisten the heart with Ringer. Usually the pericardium will be cut and it can easily be pushed over the heart. If not, pick up the pericardium, *not* the heart,

50

with the forceps and make a little snip with really sharp scissors, and enlarge the incision in the pericardium from the apex to the base of the heart.

Pin down the preparation firmly on the frog board (which has been clamped on the pillar) so that the heart now exposed lies directly below the clip which is hanging from the recording lever clamped to the pillar. By pressing the upper part of the clip the jaws will open; release the pressure and allow the clip to grip the extreme apex of the ventricle. The ventricle must not be gripped between the forceps during this manœuvre or at any other time. Ringer solution must be applied at regular intervals to keep the surface moist. Use a glass pipette with a teat. If the heart is allowed to dry, the surface sheen will disappear. This is a danger signal.

Gently raise the lever on the pillar till the thread is just tight, and cut through the fraenum. The thread should be vertical and

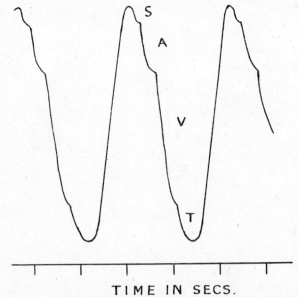

TIME IN SECS.

Make a time-trace in seconds or half seconds. Only a preparation carefully handled will show the waves well

sufficiently tight to give a good movement of the writing point; the mean position of the writing lever must be horizontal. Use the fastest drum speed on the *low* gear (surface speed one inch per

second). Using the movable base-piece of the pillar bring the writing point of the lever lightly against the drum. Screw up or down the adjustable feet of the drum so that the point of the writing lever moves in a plane parallel to the drum face. If the movements are too small then the thread holding the heart clip may be tied to the lever at a point nearer the fulcrum.

Observe the order of contraction of the various chambers of the heart and label the corresponding waves on the tracing. This will be most easily accomplished if one partner watches the heart and calls out "auricle" and "ventricle" when the chambers are seen to contract; the other partner observes the tracing as it is being written out and labels the waves accordingly.

Note that the tracing is the algebraic summation of all the contractions, so that it may happen that if one chamber is contracting while another is relaxing then the lever may remain stationary.

Effect of Adrenaline and Acetylcholine on the Heart.

(11) Use a slower drum speed than used in the previous experiment—low gear and medium pulley to medium ($\frac{1}{4}$ in. per sec.). Without stopping the drum drop a small amount of a freshly prepared solution of acetylcholine (A.Ch.) in frog Ringer over the heart. When an effect has been obtained immediately wash off the A.Ch. with ordinary Ringer. A similar effect can be obtained by using 0·1 per cent. eserine sulphate; wash with ordinary Ringer. When two traces have been obtained demonstrate the antagonism of A.Ch. and atropine thus. With the drum running drop on the heart the quantity of A.Ch. which you now know causes a fairly rapid slowing; then, when the heart is brought to a standstill, immediately drop on the atropine sulphate solution. Atropine once applied cannot readily be washed out of the tissues. Try the effect of A.Ch. again. Find the effect the solution of adrenaline provided. Mark the time of application and of removal of the drugs by means of short vertical strokes placed immediately below the trace.

Initiation of Contraction. (Stannius Ligatures Experiment.)

(12) Drum speed about $\frac{1}{4}$ in. per sec. While the heart is suspended vertically pass a thread by means of a needle or a fine forceps between the aortae (nearer the head) and the veins (caudad). Tie the first part of a reef-knot *loosely* over the line dividing sinus

from auricles (the crescent). Tie a similar loose knot around the vertical thread to the recording lever, and slide it down till it lies just below the shoulder of the ventricle. Adjust the position of the lever so that a good record is obtained *without stretching the heart*. Record a few contractions; with the drum still running tighten the first ligature to separate the sinus from the auricles. See that the knot lies actually on the crescent, and does not merely separate veins from sinus. The heart will stop beating. After, say, 10 or 15 seconds tighten the second ligature, without disturbing the recording lever, so as to separate the auricles from the ventricle. The ventricle should begin beating slowly at once or after a few minutes' delay.

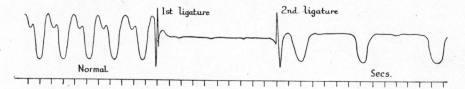

Discuss the initiation of contraction, pacemaker, heart block, the differences in fundamental or natural rate of contraction of various parts of the heart, and the effect of the drugs used.

The Nerve Supply and Control of the Heart.

(13) In the frog the origin of the accelerator and vagal fibres is probably in the medulla. The vagal and sympathetic nerves join to form one nerve which passes to the heart and enters it at the white crescentic line between the sinus and the auricles.

Connect the primary terminals of the induction coil to the I terminals (or Neef's hammer), put a shorting switch across the secondary terminals, and connect the pin electrodes across the switch.

Pith the frog and suspend the heart as before. Pass a fine forceps between the aortae and the venae cavae from one side to the other, grasp a narrow piece of tin-foil and pull it back between the vessels. Cover the liver with a piece of waxed paper, and keep this in position by pushing the fixing pins of the pin electrodes through the paper into the frog board. Twist the free end of the piece of tin-foil round one of the pin electrodes. Twist another piece of tin-foil round the other pin electrode and lay its free end on the crescent; it must not touch the frog except at the crescent.

The current induced in the secondary circuit will thus pass through the sinoauricular junction, and so stimulate the nerve fibres there.

Record first of all normal contractions on a fairly slow drum ($\frac{1}{4}$ in. per sec.); then while the drum is running stimulate the crescent with varying strengths of current beginning with a very weak one and record the effect. Always mark the beginning and end of stimulation with little vertical strokes placed immediately below the trace at the time of opening and closing the secondary shorting switch. It will usually be found that a fairly strong current is necessary to produce an effect on the rate or amplitude. It is important to increase the strength slowly, as too powerful a current may result in a prolonged inhibition of the heart. As the fibres affected by the current may be sympathetic, vagal, or both, the effect obtained may vary considerably. If the effect is acceleration, put on the heart one drop of 0·05 per cent. ergotoxine, which paralyses motor sympathetic nerves. Stimulate the crescent again and record the effect. If the original effect is slowing, then put on the heart one drop of 0·05 per cent. atropine sulphate and stimulate once more. The drugs will be supplied made up in frog-Ringer. Keep the heart moist with Ringer's solution during the course of the experiment, but do not apply it to the heart immediately after putting on ergotoxine or atropine, as the drug may be washed out of the tissues.

The Effect of Temperature on the Frog Heart.

(14) Wash the heart with Ringer to get rid of the drugs as far as possible. Take a record of the contractions and note the room temperature. Repeat this after the application of Ringer's solution at 0° C., at room temperature, and at 30° C. (not higher). Note the changes and try to account for them.

Refractory Period of Cardiac Muscle.

(15) Expose the heart and suspend it in the usual way; make records on the fastest drum on the low gear (peripheral speed 1 in. per sec.). Connect a signal (i.e. a time-marker) to the C terminals (accumulator) and adjust its height so that it writes about a quarter of an inch below the heart trace but in the same vertical line as the writing point of the heart lever. Loop one piece of tin-foil round the base of the ventricle and attach another to the metal heart clip on the apex. Attach the free ends of the pieces of tin-foil to the pin electrodes. Connect the primary coil of the

induction coil to the C terminals (accumulator). Find the position of the secondary coil which produces a "break" shock just sufficient to cause a ventricular contraction during diastole. Now watch the tracing closely while holding the primary switch. When the heart is beating regularly send in an impulse during ventricular systole, then a few beats later during early diastole, then in late diastole. The exact moment of sending in "make" and "break" shocks will be recorded by the signal by a down stroke and an up stroke respectively. There is a compensatory pause after each extra-systole. Run a time-trace and measure the various time intervals. Measure the time from the beat before an extrasystole to the beat after it, and compare with the time between one spontaneous beat and the second beat after it. Find, if possible, what happens to the auricular wave during the compensatory pause. Is the electrical stimulus effective in early ventricular systole?

Latent Period in Cardiac Muscle.

(16) Continue with the same preparation as above. Remove the tin-foil temporarily and tie the first Stannius ligature to bring the heart to a standstill. Stimulate the ventricle by scratching it gently with a needle. The scratching will pull down the lever a little and so mark the moment of stimulation. Run a time-trace and measure the latent period in several experiments.

(17) Replace the tin-foil exactly as in the previous experiment; connect the primary coil to the C terminals (accumulator) and send in single shocks by opening and closing the switch. The signal will indicate the moment of sending in the shock. Measure the latent period again.

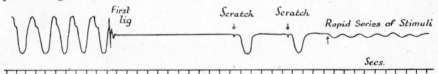

(18) Now connect the coil to the I terminals (Neef's hammer) to send in a rapid series of induced currents. Compare the record with that obtained under similar circumstances from the frog's gastrocnemius.

All-or-nothing Law.

(19) Change back to the C terminals (disconnect Neef's hammer). Put the lever very lightly against a stationary drum. Send in a

single "break" shock. If this is effective in making the heart contract take the secondary coil 1 cm. farther away from the primary, move the drum round a little by hand, wait 15 seconds, and then send in another "break" shock. At intervals of 15 seconds send in progressively weaker shocks, recording the results till no effect is obtained. Discuss the relationship between strength of stimulus and response and compare with the similar experiment on skeletal muscle.

The Automatic Action of the Frog's Heart.

(20) Remove the heart clip. Count the heart rate in beats per minute. Cut the heart out of the body, keeping the scissors well away from the bulbus and sinus but avoiding the gall-bladder. Put it in a watch-glass containing Ringer's solution. Note the sequence of contraction of the various parts of the heart, and again count the heart rate. Cut through the sinoauricular junction, count the rate of the sinus contractions and compare with that of the remainder of the heart. Cut through the auriculoventricular junction just above the auriculoventricular groove and report on the behaviour of the various parts. Separate the lower two-thirds of the ventricle. Report on its behaviour and the effect of stimulation, both electrical and mechanical.

PERFUSION OF FROG'S BLOOD VESSELS

(21) Use Marriotte's flask connected by rubber tubing to a special cannula. Fill the Marriotte's flask with frog-Ringer solution after clamping the rubber tubing. Insert the stopper carrying the central glass tube.

Kill a frog and crush the head. Pin it down on the shovel-shaped board. Expose the heart by removing the sternum. Pass a thread under one of the aortae and tie very loosely the first half of a reef-knot. Slack off the clamp on the rubber tubing, and after clearing out all air bubbles adjust it so that there is a very slow drip from the cannula. Test your scissors to see that they cut to the very point. If so make a cut somewhat obliquely into the aorta, cutting it about half way through. Insert the cannula into this incision and push it down into the distal end of the aorta and tie the ligature firmly. Tie a ligature round the other aorta and make a cut into the venous end of the heart. Raise the Marriotte's flask to about 40 cm. above the cannula.

The perfusion fluid will begin to drip off the frog board. The rate of flow may be recorded either by counting the number of drops falling per half minute or by collecting them in a measuring cylinder and noting the level at minute or half-minute intervals throughout the experiment. The perfusion pressure will be kept constant by the Marriotte's flask in spite of the fall of the level of fluid within. Why?

The effect of adrenaline $1:10^6$ or acetylcholine $1:10^6$ can be shown by perfusing them instead of the normal Ringer; or small quantities of more concentrated solutions (1 c.c. of $1:10^5$) can be injected by means of a syringe through the rubber tubing just above the cannula. After perfusing a drug perfuse with Ringer's solution for some time to get back if possible to the original rate of flow. Find the effect of injecting 1 c.c. of 0.5 per cent. sodium nitrite. As the experiment proceeds fluid will escape from the blood vessels into the tissues which will become swollen and tense, i.e. oedematous. The perfusion rate will become less and less and the preparation will become useless for the demonstration of the action of the drugs.

If the preparation is still in good condition pith the animal and note if this produces any difference in flow. Has adrenaline any effect now?

· Describe the action of the various drugs and say whether their action is local or central. What is the cause of the oedema, and why does it slow up the flow?

PERFUSION OF FROG'S HEART

(**21a**) The apparatus of (**21**) may be used to perfuse the frog's heart. Suspend the heart as in (**10**) and pass a loose ligature round the posterior vena cava. Fill the special cannula with Ringer and make a cut half through the vena cava, not too near the sinus. Insert the cannula and tie in position. If this ligature is near the crescent the heart will stop. If the cannula is correctly inserted the auricle will swell up. Cut across both aortae. Adjust the Marriotte's flask so that the lower end of the central tube is about 2 cm. above the auricle. The cardiac movements are recorded as in (**10**). The outside of the heart must be kept moist with Ringer.

Find the effect of perfusing with adrenaline $1:10^6$ or A.Ch. $1:10^6$. The effect of eserine and atropine can be tested out as (**11**).

E

CHAPTER THREE

SMOOTH MUSCLE

Contraction of Visceral Muscle in the Frog.

(22) KILL and decerebrate a frog but do not pith it. Fix it belly up to the frog board by pinning down the arms and by pushing a pin through or just above the symphysis pubis, but put no pins in the legs as these may be used later for muscle-nerve preparations.

Make a mid-line incision in the abdominal wall and cut through the rectum at its junction with the small intestine, and attach the clip of a frog heart lever to the cut end of the rectum so that its movements may be recorded. Drive the drum from the shafting itself to the largest pulley on the low gear so as to obtain the slowest possible drum. As the movements of the rectum are very slow indeed they may not be at all obvious unless they are

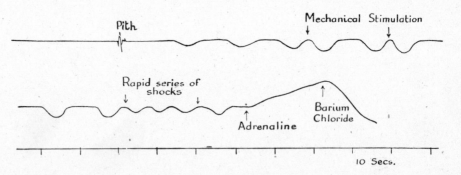

recorded. If the record is a straight line at first it is wise to continue recording for five minutes, when it may show waves. Tap the bench lightly at short intervals so that the friction at the point of the lever is diminished. Keep the rectum moist with Ringer. If no movements are obtained pour warm Ringer over the rectum. Without disturbing the apparatus pith the frog and continue to record the rectal movements.

Place two loops of tin-foil around the gut about 1 cm. apart,

66

and connect them to pin electrodes. Try to stimulate the smooth muscle of the rectum by connecting the pin electrodes to the G terminals for 1 second. Then stimulate mechanically by pinching with forceps. Try to tetanise the muscle by a rapid series of induced currents. Apply a drop of adrenaline (1 in 1000) to the rectum with a glass rod. Then similarly apply a drop of 2 per cent. barium chloride solution.

(23) Cut through the small intestine at its junction with the stomach and attach the heart clip to the pyloric end of the stomach. The oesophageal end is fairly well fixed to the tissues of the frog. Keep the stomach moist with warm Ringer solution at, say, 28° C. Observe the peristaltic waves. Draw deductions concerning the rate of movement, latent period, effect of rapid series of stimuli, effect of drugs on smooth muscle. Compare with cardiac and skeletal muscle when you have done the corresponding experiments.

Effect of Adrenaline on the Frog's Eye.

(24) Split a frog's head so as to divide it into two portions each containing an eye. Put one eye into a watch-glass containing ordinary Ringer, the other into a watch-glass containing Ringer with a drop of adrenaline (1 in 1000). Put both into the cupboard. After 10 minutes note any difference in the pupils.

(25) This experiment may be repeated, using fresh eyes and solutions of 1 per cent. eserine and 1 per cent. atropine (in Ringer).

MAMMALIAN INTESTINAL MUSCLE IN VITRO

(26) The apparatus consists of a central vessel of 100 c.c. capacity with an outlet at its lower end for draining off the fluid. The central vessel is enclosed in a large beaker of water which is kept at 37° C. by means of a small gas flame, or better by an adjustable carbon filament electric lamp. A hollow glass tube fitted with a hook at its lower end is clamped to a pillar by a boss head so that it can be lowered into the central vessel. The pillar also carries a balanced lever with a swivel writing point giving a magnification of about three or four times.

Fill the central vessel with Locke's solution at 37° C. and the outer vessel with water from the tap at 37° C. See that the temperature of the inner vessel is maintained at 37° C. by varying the size of the flame or the position of the heating

lamp. Raise the hooked glass tube out of the central vessel. Have ready a Petri dish with warm Tyrode and a threaded needle.

The rabbit will be killed. All the following procedures must be carried out with the greatest delicacy to avoid stretching the gut. Remove very gently portions of jejunum, minus mesentery. Syringe gently with Tyrode's solution through the pieces to remove the intestinal contents and at once place in Tyrode's solution. Cut off a piece of gut about 1 in. long and pass a threaded needle through all the coats near one end from the inside to the outside, make a short loop. Pass another thread through the other end, tie and leave about 6 in. of thread. In tying the threads do not close off the lumen of the gut. Pass the loop over the hook and lower the tube down into the warm Tyrode, lower the lever to a suitable position and fasten the long thread to the lever by pressing it into a small lump of plasticine. Adjust the weight (a piece of plasticine) on the lever so that the gut is just stretched. See that the gut is completely immersed. Attach the air supply pipe to the hollow tube and adjust the screw clamp till about three bubbles per second pass through the fluid. This aerates and stirs the fluid.

Record the movements on a slowly moving drum. It may be necessary to wait a few minutes for the movements to become fairly regular. Keep the temperature at 37° C. and see that the aeration is maintained. In the meantime keep a supply of fresh Tyrode in a bottle at 37° C. by immersing the bottle in a basin of warm water.

While the lever is recording add to the bath 1 c.c. of 1:100,000 adrenaline solution by means of a 1-c.c. pipette. Make a mark below the record at the time of adding the solution. The concentration in the bath will be 1 in 10^7. When an effect is obtained drain off the Tyrode and immediately replace with fresh warm solution. If the dose of adrenaline is insufficient to produce an effect make up a 1 in 10,000 solution and add small quantities of this to the bath. Not more than 1 c.c. of a solution of a drug should be added to the bath at any time to avoid sudden changes of temperature.

When the gut is contracting rhythmically once more add Acetylcholine (A.Ch.) to give a concentration of 1 in 10^7. If an effect is obtained, drain off the Tyrode and replace once more.

These observations should be repeated to give a trace for each partner. Then add to the bath a dose of A.Ch., which produces a well-marked contraction. When this has reached its peak add to

the bath 1 c.c. $1:10^4$ atropine sulphate. This experiment will have to be repeated on a fresh piece of gut as the action of atropine is very prolonged.

Observe the effect on the contractions of magnesium sulphate.

What is the cause of the intestinal movements? How are they controlled? Discuss the reasons for keeping the temperature at 37° C. and using Locke's or Tyrode's solution.

THE MOVEMENTS OF THE UTERUS IN VITRO

(27) These movements can be recorded exactly as described for the gut. The virgin guinea-pig uterus is used to compare solutions containing an unknown quantity of oxytocin with standard solutions—a biological assay.

The procedure is as with gut, but since the movements are very slow it will be necessary to introduce an external reduction gear so that the drum travels about quarter of an inch per minute. The virgin guinea-pig uterus is quiescent at the beginning of an experiment and shows the action of posterior pituitary extract well (0·03 unit added to the bath). Study also the action of adrenaline and histamine on this preparation. If virgin guinea-pigs are not available, stock animals will usually give very active uteri. The amplitude is less if a half horn instead of a whole horn is used.

NOTE ON USE OF DRUGS : METHOD OF CALCULATING DILUTIONS

Always add the minimum amount consistent with accuracy. This avoids temperature, osmotic, salt and other changes. The inner vessel of the mammalian apparatus has a capacity of 100 ml. A ml. of the usual fluids is taken to weigh 1 g. Suppose 0·05 ml. of 1:1,000 adrenaline solution is added to 100 ml. Tyrode. What will be the concentration of adrenaline in the Tyrode? 1:1,000 adrenaline solution means 1 g. adrenaline in 1,000 g. fluid, or 1/1,000 g. in 1 ml. fluid, or 1/10,000 g. in 0·1 ml. fluid, or 1/20,000 g. in 0·05 ml. fluid, the amount you are going to add to the Tyrode. 1/20,000 g. in 100 ml. is similar in dilution to 1 g. adrenaline in 20,000× 100 ml., i.e. 2,000,000 ml. So dilution is 1 in 2,000,000 or 1 in 2×10^6.

Suppose you are told to add such a quantity of adrenaline that the concentration in a bath of 100 ml. Tyrode will be 1 in 1,000,000. This means that each ml. in the bath should have 1/1,000,000 g. adrenaline. Whole bath should have 100/1,000,000 g. or 1/10,000 g. If adrenaline supplied is already diluted 1:1,000, this means that each ml. has 1/1,000 g. adrenaline. Then 0·1 ml. of the adrenaline solution supplied has 1/10,000 g. of adrenaline, the amount which should be present in the whole bath. If your syringe is accurate you may be able to add 0·1 ml. adrenaline solution as such. If your syringe is not very accurate, draw into syringe 0·5 ml. adrenaline solution at 1:1,000, eject this into an accurate measuring cylinder and add Tyrode to 5 ml. Mix. Then 1 ml. of this mixture will contain 0·1 ml. of adrenaline 1:1,000, i.e. 1/10,000 g. adrenaline, the amount required.

CHAPTER FOUR

THE CENTRAL NERVOUS SYSTEM

Reflex Action in the Frog.

(28) (1) Study the behaviour of the intact frog and its response to stimulation of various kinds. Note how it rights itself after having been placed on its back. Observe respiration.

(2) Remove the hemispheres preferably by crushing the head up to a line running just behind the eyes. After the shock of the operation has passed off examine the frog's behaviour once more. Do respiratory movements continue? If very active this preparation may swim in a basin of water. Place the frog on a rough board or on the frog board, tilt the board, the frog will slowly move up.

(3) Wrap the frog in a duster and hold it belly upwards. Open its mouth. There is a small triangular elevation on the roof of the mouth between the eye and the tympanic membrane. To destroy the semi-circular canals insert the closed blades of a fine scissors about 2 mm. deep into this elevation, open the blades a little and turn them round about two or three times. Observe the behaviour with the canals destroyed on one side.

(4) Decerebrate the frog by cutting off the head behind the tympanic membranes and proceed to the next experiments. After the shock has passed off describe the attitude and behaviour of the spinal frog. Pin it up by the lower jaw to the edge of the frog board so that the legs are about 5 inches above the bench. Observe the position of the legs. Apply a small piece ($\frac{1}{4}$ in. $\times \frac{1}{4}$ in.) of blotting-paper soaked in 10 per cent. acetic acid to the flank of the frog. Note how the irritating object is removed by co-ordinated movements of the limbs.

(5) Pinch one toe gently with fine forceps, then more and more forcibly. Observe the extent of the response, also the spread and duration of the response.

(6) Raise the frog's foot with the end of a pencil. Some frogs show a thrust reflex.

(7) Türck's time of reflex action. Have ready three jars: *a*, plain water; *b*, weak acid (0·5 per cent. sulphuric acid); *c*, stronger acid (1 per cent. sulphuric acid). Hold jar *b* so that the acid covers the frog's legs to just over the knees. Count seconds, 0, 1, 2, 3, etc., till reflex action is elicited. Then wash off acid with *a*. Similarly try the effect of *c*, counting the time as before. Wash off with *a*.

(8) Connect up the induction coil to the C terminals (accumulator). Push the pin electrodes through the skin of a foot. Very slowly (once in four seconds, say) move up and down the switch on the terminal board to elicit reflex withdrawal. Move the secondary coil away from the primary till the stimulus is just too weak to elicit reflex action. (Distinguish carefully reflex withdrawal from any local contraction of the muscles of the foot due to direct stimulation.) This is a subminimal stimulus. Change over to the I terminals (or Neef's hammer) and send in a series of subminimal stimuli. Describe the effect.

(9) Make a longitudinal incision in the skin on the back of the thigh by clipping off a piece of skin held up in a forceps. With a glass rod moistened with Ringer solution separate the two groups of muscles (flexors and extensors) and raise the sciatic nerve. Pass a cotton thread under the nerve without tying so that it can be raised to pass pin electrodes under the nerve later. Push the pin electrodes into the foot, connect the coil to I terminals (Neef's hammer) and send in a series of strong induced currents until the withdrawal reflex is fatigued. Reduce the strength of the induced current by moving the secondary coil about 10 cm. farther from the primary coil. Quickly insert the electrodes under the sciatic nerve. There will be an immediate muscular response. The fatigue does not appear to be resident in the outgoing nerve, and by analogy not in the ingoing nerve to the cord. Suggest possible sites and causes of the fatigue.

(10) Irradiation of reflexes has already been noted (5). With strong scissors cut across the spinal cord below the level of entrance of the nerves to the fore limbs—i.e. on a line joining the posterior (caudal) borders of the fore limbs. Pinch the fore limbs vigorously and then the legs. How do the responses differ from those previously obtained? Give reasons for this.

(11) Take the frog's limbs gently between the fingers and try to estimate the tone of the muscles. Pith the frog and note the difference in tone. Is it possible to elicit any reflexes?

Experiments on the Human Subject.

From this point onwards many of the experiments will be performed on the human subject.

As a clinical investigation is really in the nature of an experiment on the human subject it would be well for the student to adopt from the beginning in the physiological laboratory the proper mental attitude to his subject or patient.

Ignorance of some of the psychological considerations noted below is often shown by students both in the laboratory and in the ward.

Many activities of the lower levels of the central nervous system can easily be modified consciously. For example, when testing spinal reflexes the subject must be kept at his ease both mentally and physically, and his attention should be directed away from the part under investigation.

We are accustomed, normally, to take in information from several senses— eyes, ears, skin, etc. When investigating any one sense it is the duty of the experimenter to see that the subject does not consciously, or unconsciously, obtain information from other sources. In other words, the observer must see that the subject does not "cheat."

The subject must be given precise and simple instructions. Patients have no knowledge of physiological terminology. It is merely stupid to tell a patient (or the subject) to "focus on a near object." The best way is to hold a finger in front of his face and to give the simple direct instruction, "Look at my finger."

These are important points in both physiological and clinical investigations. In addition it is to be remembered always that the patient is a fellow human being and not an experimental animal, and that if he is persuaded to come before the class so that his reflexes, for example, can be demonstrated he must be treated with consideration by the class during what is for him something of an ordeal.

Reflexes in the Human Subject.

If a normal reflex is obtained it indicates that the reflex path —sense organ or receptor, ingoing nerve, connections in central nervous system, outgoing nerve, muscle or effector—is intact. Reflexes may be exaggerated, diminished or altered. It is important to know the normal reflex in order that any departure from it may be readily recognised.

(**29**) (1) Cutaneous or superficial reflexes. These cannot be tested in the class but must be tried out at home.

(a) *Plantar reflex.*—Scratch the sole of the foot near the inner side. All the toes become plantar flexed. If the hallux is pointed upwards and the other toes fanned, this is described as the positive Babinski's sign or the extensor type of plantar response, and in the waking adult subject indicates damage to the pyramidal fibres.

(b) *Abdominal reflex.*—Stroke the skin of the abdominal wall. The reflex contraction of the abdominal muscles will pull the umbilicus to the side stroked.

(c) *Cremasteric reflex.*—Stroke the inner side of the thigh. There will be a contraction of the cremaster muscle.

(2) Tendon or deep reflexes.

(a) *Knee jerk.*—The subject must be seated in a chair or on a stool of moderate height, with legs dangling or with one leg crossed over the other. He must not be in a strained position, and if possible his attention should be diverted from the experiment. With the tendon hammer hit the patellar tendon just below the patella. The extensor muscles will contract and the foot will be kicked forward. If no reflex is obtained then ask the subject to hook his fingers together and to pull them apart. Try again to elicit the reflex.

(b) *Achilles jerk.*—The subject kneels on a chair so that both legs are supported but the feet hang free. Hit the tendo Achillis smartly with the tendon hammer and note the movement of the foot caused by the contraction of the gastrocnemius muscle.

(c) *Biceps jerk.*—Ask the subject to let his arm lie slackly, his forearm supported on your left forearm while you steady his elbow on the palm of your left hand. Place your left thumb on the biceps tendon, and hit your thumb with the hammer. The biceps will contract and make the tendon tense under your finger.

(d) *Triceps jerk.*—The subject's arm should lie slackly. Support his upper arm in a horizontal position with your left hand and let his forearm hang vertically down. Tap the triceps tendon just above the elbow joint and note the movement of the arm.

3. Eye reflexes. (Organic reflexes include the pupillary reflexes of the eye, and the reflexes involved in micturition and defaecation, etc.) (*a*) Have the subject facing the window. Look at his eyes and note the iris (the coloured part) and the size of the pupil. With your two hands cover *both* eyes for ten seconds. Instruct the subject to keep looking at a distant object. Then remove one hand and observe the pupil. Repeat the procedure for the other eye. This is the direct light reflex. (*b*) Keep the subject in the same position and cover both eyes again. Stand to one side and raise one hand slightly to observe the pupil but not so much as to let light from the window into this eye. Remove the hand entirely from the other eye while continuing to observe the pupil of the first eye. This is the consensual light reflex. (*c*) Reaction on accommodation or convergence. Turn the subject so that he is facing a dully illuminated wall. Ask him to look at the wall and then at your finger held about six inches from his eyes slightly

F

above eye level (to keep the upper lid raised). Observe the change in the pupils. (*d*) The corneal and conjunctival reflexes are really superficial reflexes. Gently touch the periphery of the cornea, or the sclerotic, with the corner of a clean handkerchief or a piece of clean paper. The eyelids close immediately; if the stimulus is more intense there will be lachrymation.

These are the reflexes usually tested in the routine examination of a patient. Describe the normal reflexes, and indicate which part of the central nervous system is involved in each.

Cranial Nerves.

(**30**) For the localisation of cranial disorders it is important to know the normal function of the cranial nerves. Many of the tests will be described in various sections of this book. The following nerves are not specially referred to: V, VII, IX, XI, XII. Bearing in mind the remarks on p. 78, and using your knowledge of anatomy, demonstrate the normal function of these nerves in your partner. For example, in the case of the trigeminal nerve, find if the sensation of touch is present over the area supplied by the nerve and ask the subject to move his mandible as in chewing.

REACTION TIMES

The reaction time is the time elapsing between the reception of a sensory stimulus and the acting upon it.

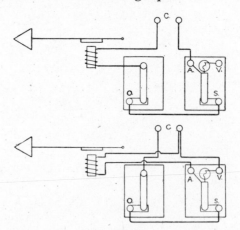

Connect up the two spring switches and an electromagnetic signal (time-marker) to C terminals (accumulator) as indicated

in the upper diagram on page 82. O is the observer's switch; S is the subject's switch with a flash-lamp bulb which can be brought into circuit by connecting to V (= visual). For auditory and touch reaction times use terminal A.

(**31**) *Auditory Reaction Time.*—Use the fastest possible drum speed. Join A to a C terminal. The subject must be placed so that he cannot see the drum; he depresses switch S and keeps it closed. While the drum is running and the signal writing on it, the observer closes switch O and keeps it down. When the subject hears the click of the armature against the magnets he opens S as quickly as possible. Run a time-trace with the 100 per second fork. Measure the time in σ, thousandths of a second. Repeat at least three times. Does practice improve the result?

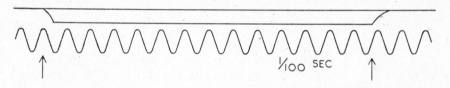

1/100 SEC

(**32**) *Visual Reaction Time.*—Join V to a C terminal (accumulator) and see that the lamp lights when the circuit is completed. If the lamp glows only feebly then the time-marker resistance is rather high, and it will be better to put the marker across the lamp so that both get the full voltage of C terminals (lower diagram, p. 82). Quieten the signal by standing it on a folded duster. Proceed as before, closing the key quietly but firmly; the subject must open switch S when he sees the lamp glow. Repeat and measure.

(**33**) *Touch Reaction Time.*—Remove switch O and replace by the brass touch contact switch. When the subject's hand is touched with this the conical brass end is pressed against a contact inside the pencil-shaped barrel. Normally the conical end is kept out of contact by a very light spring. Muffle the signal and proceed as before; the observer must keep the "pencil" pressed against the subject till he responds. This time the subject releases S when he feels the touch. Repeat and measure.

Tabulate your results for all experiments. In order to give these figures a meaning for everyday affairs, take the shortest time for the light reaction and calculate the distance in yards travelled in that time by a motor car driven at 30 m.p.h. This will give the distance traversed before you could *begin* to apply the brake after

receiving a warning light signal when travelling at 30 m.p.h. Note that this is only part of the distance required to bring the car to a standstill. A car travelling at 30 m.p.h. can be stopped in 30 feet from the moment of application of the brake, assuming 100 per cent. braking efficiency with optimum coefficient of friction between the tyres and the road.

Make measurements as accurately as you can of the length of the pathways concerned in these reaction tests. Does the time spent in travelling up and down these paths account for all of the time you have just measured?

Reaction times quoted from Myers:

Stimulus.	Muscular Reaction.* σ	Sensorial Reaction.† σ
Sound . . .	125	220
Light . . .	175	270
Touch . . .	110	210
Heat . . .	130	190
Cold . . .	115	150

* Attention given to movement for response.
† Attention given to stimulus about to be received.

The Effect of Prolonged Exercise (Mosso's Ergograph).

(34) Insert the first and third fingers into the fixed tubes and the second finger into the hinged middle tube of the apparatus. Strap the forearm in position. The middle tube is hinged so that when the finger is flexed it pulls a writing lever over the surface of a drum, and at the same time it raises a weight (3 kilograms). In the case of women students a smaller weight will be used. The drum is laid on its side and is driven as slowly as possible. The drum with its record should be screened from the subject. Connect a lamp to the T terminals so that it flashes for a brief period every two seconds. Flex the finger each time the light flashes, and continue until fatigue is so great that the weight can no longer be moved. At this point stimulate the flexors electrically. Can the flexors be made to contract and lift the weight? Describe the shape and the duration of the record obtained and draw conclusions about them.

(35) The value of rest pauses in work can be well shown with this apparatus. The rest pause used in the army is five minutes in every hour. One can keep the same ratio of rest to work by repeat-

ing the first experiment but resting during five seconds every minute. It will be found that the experiment can be carried on for a greatly extended period. Measure the total length of all the lines in the first experiment to get the total distance that the 3-kilogram weight has been lifted, and calculate the work done. Compare with the work done in the second experiment.

CHAPTER FIVE

SPECIAL SENSES (EXCLUDING VISION)

CUTANEOUS SENSES

AT this meeting one student will act as experimenter or observer and his partner as subject, but the results recorded in your book should be those obtained when you were acting as subject.

It is the duty of the observer to see that his subject's answers are accurate and honest and based on the sensation arising in the end organ under investigation, and that they are not dependent on the subject's expectations (conscious or unconscious) or on information reaching him *via* another end organ (e.g. the eye).

General definitions. A stimulus is an environmental change capable of, or potentially capable of, inducing a change in living tissues. A reaction is a response to a stimulus. A sensation is a change in consciousness.

It is to be noted that many of the tests described below, although at first sight appearing simple and often obvious, are those actually employed in clinical investigations. It is a great advantage at the bedside to have simple tests requiring relatively little apparatus.

Temperature Sense.

(36) Prepare three jars of water in the order hot, warm, cold. The water in the first should be as hot as can be borne by the finger without pain. Dip the right forefinger in cold, the left in hot. After one minute place both together in warm. Record your sensations. The human temperature sense is relative and not absolute; in this experiment it appears to depend on the rate of abstraction of heat from, or of addition of heat to, the skin.

(37) Compare the temperature sensations given by a piece of flannel and a piece of metal at room temperature. Try to explain this on the same lines as before.

(**38**) Use the rubber stamp to map out an area on the back of the hand between any two metacarpals. Apply the stamp to your book. Trail the chilled blunt-ended brass rod gently across the area mapped out. Mark on the diagram in your book spots at which a cold sensation is appreciated. Heat the brass rod to about 45° C. and again explore and record the "hot" spots. Repeat these observations after the hand has been held in (*a*) hot water, (*b*) cold water, for three minutes. Are the "spots" fixed in position?

(**39**) Have two large glass test-tubes containing water at 36° and 38° C. Apply these to the face of the subject in turn. He will be able to tell easily which is warmer. Then add cold water gradually to the warmer until he is no longer able to appreciate the difference. What is the minimum perceptible difference?

Sense of Contact.

(**40**) Apply the rubber stamp to (*a*) volar surface of distal phalanx of thumb, (*b*) back of hand, (*c*) back of forearm; also make stamps in your book for records. Make a map of the touch spots in these areas by exploring them with von Frey's bristles. These are hairs of several thicknesses mounted at the end of match sticks; the observer holds the match stick and touches the subject's skin with the end of the hair, applying gentle pressure just sufficient to make the hair bend. The subject indicates when he is certain he feels a contact. Explore first of all with a fine bristle and then with a thick one.

(**41**) Compare the sensations when a small piece of loose cotton wool is lightly stroked over the back of the hand and the palm of the hand (a hairy and a hairless part).

(**42**) You are provided with two sets of weights, one ranging around 40 gm., the other around 80 gm. The actual mass is marked on each. The subject with eyes closed lays his hand on the bench *palmar surface up*, with the fingers a little apart; the dorsal aspect of the fingers must be kept in contact with the bench throughout the experiment. Head three columns on a piece of paper 1, 2, answer. The observer lays weight 40 on the middle phalanx of the middle finger for three seconds; after five seconds he applies another weight in the same range for three seconds. Enter the weights in the table in the order of application to the finger and also the subject's impression of the second weight—lighter, heavier, same. Repeat twenty times with various weights,

and occasionally use the same weight twice. Determine the smallest percentage difference that can be appreciated with accuracy.

Repeat the experiment with the 80 set and compare the result with that obtained with the 40 range.

(**43**) Apply the 40-gm. weight, then the 80 and then the 40. Ask the subject whether the third was lighter, heavier, or the same as the first. Repeat in the order 40, 20, 40; then 40, 40, 40. What is the influence of the second stimulus?

(**44**) With the aesthesiometer (dividers) test the subject's discrimination. Vary the distance apart of the points; apply both points *simultaneously* and lightly. Test the back of the hand, the volar surface of distal phalanx of the thumb, and the back of the forearm. Vary the distance between the points irregularly. Record the distance in one column, and the subject's answer—"one," "two," "don't know"—in another column. Determine the smallest interval appreciated with certainty on the three areas. Measure the distance apart of the touch spots in the diagrams obtained previously. What relation do these distances bear to the figures obtained now?

(**45**) Aristotle's experiment. The subject closes his eyes, crosses the middle finger over the index finger. The observer lays a pencil in the space between the finger tips. The subject describes his sensation.

(**46**) A large-toothed wheel (100 teeth) is driven by a motor controlled by a resistance calibrated in revolutions per second. Lay a finger *lightly* on the wheel and increase the speed until the wheel appears smooth. Calculate the number of stimuli per second at which the sensations fuse to a continuous sensation.

(**47**) Compare the sensations when a kilogram weight is allowed to fall from 5 cm. and from 20 cm. into the hand.

(**48**) Strike a 100 per second tuning-fork and hold the vibrating end against a hair on the back of the hand. When the sensation is at an end move the fork to another hair. Record the sensation. Discuss adaptation. Note that this is *not* a method of testing vibration sensibility.

Sense of Pain.

(**49**) Using a needle mounted on a piece of cork make a map of the pain spots in the same areas as explored in testing the sense of contact.

From these and previous experiments could you decide what would be a suitable area for puncture of the skin preparatory to a hypodermic injection.

Do the pain, temperature, and touch spots coincide?

PROPRIOCEPTIVE SENSES

Muscle Joint Sense.

All these experiments must be performed with the subject's eyes closed.

(50) The student describes the shape of various objects placed in his hand. He attempts to copy with one hand the position of the other hand and fingers set by the observer. He stretches out his right arm to the right, and then quickly bends the arm and attempts to touch the point of his nose with the tip of the right index finger. This is repeated for the left arm and then with the eyes open.

(51) Use the two sets of weights as before (sense of contact, p. 92), but allow the subject to move the arm up and down to aid the estimation. Is his accuracy improved?

(52) The subject studies the dynamometer, then he closes his eyes and compresses the spring and gives his estimate of the force of compression. With the eyes open note the muscular tension on bringing the pointer to any convenient number. Try to bring it to the same number with the eyes closed.

Vibration Sensibility.

(53) Vibration sensibility is tested by applying the base of a vibrating tuning-fork of low pitch to a subcutaneous bony prominence. The subject indicates how long the sensation lasts.

To obtain standard results a special tuning-fork has been devised. A small notched plate is fixed to the inner aspect of the end of one prong, the notches are overlapped on both sides by a double plate fixed to the inner side of the other prong so that the notches are normally hidden. When the fork is vibrating strongly, owing to the separation of the prongs the notches will be seen as a "window" which gradually diminishes in size as the amplitude of vibration decreases. The time in seconds between the disappearance of the "window" and the end of the sensation of vibration appreciated by the patient is taken as a measure of the vibration sensibility.

G

Record the times found in your case for the radial styloid and the external malleolus and compare with the times found by other members of the class.

Labyrinthine Mechanism.

(54) The subject spins round rapidly several times. When he stops he directs his eyes in the direction to which he was spinning. The observer studies his eyes for movements and describes their character and direction. These movements are known as nystagmus. When they are active the subject should extend the right arm forward and with the index finger first with the eyes open and then with the eyes closed touch some point. The last experiment should be repeated when no nystagmus is present.

(55) Hold a short stick vertically with its point on the ground. Place the forehead on the top and walk rapidly three times round it. Then raising yourself straight, try to walk to the door. Notice the effect produced and try to explain it. Try to reach a conclusion as to how the semi-circular canals may act in the above experiments.

Taste.

(56) You are provided with (a) 5 per cent. cane sugar—sweet; (b) saturated quinine sulphate—bitter; (c) 0·5 per cent. H_2SO_4—sour; (d) 1 per cent. NaCl—salt. The subject protrudes his tongue and dries it. The observer, using small pieces of blotting-paper, paints the various solutions in turn on the tip, side, centre, back of the tongue. Record the subject's sensations on a diagram, noting also the time between the applications of the stimulus and his sensation. Tap the tip of the tongue with the point of a pencil—describe your sensation. Using nonpolarisable electrodes (Ag, AgCl) stimulate the tip of the tongue by connecting them to the G terminals (16-volt battery).

Smell.

(57) The subject closes his eyes, pinches his nose and opens his mouth; the observer places pieces of potato on the subject's tongue. These are replaced in turn by pieces of onion. The substances may be rolled over the tongue but should not be chewed because the texture is different in the two cases. The identification is noted in several tests and control experiments should be made with the nose open. Compare the results of this experiment with

the so-called loss or impairment of taste during a "cold in the head."

Speech and Hearing.

(58) There will be a demonstration of the use of the laryngoscope. The demonstrator will try to show you the movements of the vocal cords on inspiration and expiration, on saying "ah" and "ee" and on giving a little cough. Afterwards practise on the model throats and then attempt to see your partner's vocal cords. Draw a diagram to illustrate the method and another to show the relationship of the structures seen. Make a note of the antiseptic precautions used.

Hearing.—Examine the models of the ear which illustrate the movements of the ossicles.

(59) The subject covers one ear, the observer brings up a watch behind his head and notes the distance at which it is first heard; this is repeated with the other ear.

(60) *Weber's Test.*—Rest the base of a vibrating tuning-fork on the vertex and describe the sensation; close one ear and then the other with the finger and record the sensations.

(61) *Rinne's Test.*—Hold the vibrating fork with its base firmly on the mastoid process; when it is no longer heard transfer it to a position with the prongs near the outer ear, when it will be heard once more.

(62) Block one auditory meatus with a piece of wet cotton wool and repeat tests 59, 60, and 61. Suggest how these tests may be useful in localising the cause of deafness. Remove the cotton wool. To show that tests 60 and 61 depend on the masking effect of room noise place the fork on the right mastoid process, and at the moment when it becomes inaudible insert a finger in the right ear, whereupon the sound will once more be heard for a few seconds.

(63) *Upper limit of audibility.*—Determine the upper limit of audibility by means of the steel rods. Strike the rods while the ear is near them. Disregard the noise of the hitting. Note that the figures on the rods refer to half vibrations and not to complete cycles per second.

Lower limit of audibility.—Strike the 50 cycles per second tuning-fork. Can you hear the sound produced as a musical tone?

(**64**) *Localisation.*—The subject closes his eyes. The observer makes clicking noises with forceps behind the subject and asks him to locate the position. Record the results in tabular form.

(**65**) *Masking.*—Ask the subject to read from a book. After a few sentences make a rattling noise, using a tin box containing pieces of lead, near his ear. The intensity of the voice will be raised. This would not occur in a deaf person. This test is used to detect malingering.

CHAPTER SIX

PHYSIOLOGY OF VISION

Stimulation of the Retina.

(66) CLOSE the eyelids and press on the eyeball. Describe the sensation and note its position in the field of vision for comparison with the position of the part of the retina stimulated. Connect chamois leather electrodes dipped in salt solution to the secondary terminals of the induction coil (primary to C terminals). Put one electrode on the forehead, the other on the nape of the neck. Make and break the primary circuit. Describe the sensation produced.

Müller's Law of Specific Nerve Energy

Müller's law or "the law of specific nerve energy" may be summarised thus:—Different varieties of stimuli applied to the same sense organ always produce the sensation peculiar to that organ, and conversely, different sense organs excited by the same stimulus evoke only the sensation peculiar to the sense organ stimulated.

Blind Spot.

(67) (1) Make two black circles about $\frac{1}{8}$ in. diameter about 4 in. apart. Hold the paper up in front of the right eye at arm's length; close the left eye. Fix the right eye on the left-hand mark. Bring the paper slowly towards the face. The right-hand mark will disappear and then reappear as the paper is brought nearer.

(2) Rest the subject's chin on a support (e.g. a book) about 10 in. above the bench. He gazes steadily (left eye closed) at a small cross in the centre of a piece of white paper below his right eye. The observer prepares a long strip of white paper with a large ($\frac{1}{8}$ in.) black dot at one end; holding the other end he makes the black dot travel over the paper from the right towards the cross. When the dot becomes invisible to the subject and when it reappears, the observer makes a mark through the dot on to the paper below. This procedure is repeated for vertical and oblique movements of the dot across the blind area. Finally the points are

joined up to make an outline of the projected image of the blind spot. The largest diameter is measured and the actual size of the blind spot is calculated by the method of similar triangles, given that the distance between the nodal point of the eye and the retina is 15 mm. Calculate also the distance of the blind spot from the optical axis—i.e. the fovea centralis. Approximately how many times the diameter of the blind spot is this?

Observation of the Macula Lutea.

(68) Look through the bottle containing a strong solution of chrome alum at the centre of a window pane. A pink patch will appear temporarily in the field of vision. The chrome alum solution transmits only red, green and blue rays, and the blue rays are absorbed by the yellow pigment of the macula.

Inversion of the Retinal Image.

(69) Prick a hole in a piece of black paper, hold it in the left hand about 3 in. from one eye; close the other eye. Look through the hole at the sky. Hold a pin in the right hand so that its head is close to the eye between the paper and the eye. It appears to be upside down. The light coming through the hole in the paper casts a direct shadow of the pin's head on the retina, and this shadow is the same way up as the pin itself. Confirm this by repeating the experiment with a convex lens provided with a screen at its focal length (i.e. an artificial eye). This will be set up in the optical room.

Near Point.

(70) Hold a pencil in front of the eye and bring it nearer till it can no longer be seen clearly. Measure the distance to the eye. Do this again without spectacles if these are worn. Repeat this experiment at home on people of various ages. What influence does age have on the near point?

Focusing.

(71) Hold a pencil between one eye and the corner of the room. Keep the other eye closed. Attempt to focus both the corner of the room and the pencil at the same time. Illustrate the sensation by means of diagrams.

Sanson's Images.

(72) In the optical room observe the various images when a candle is held near a convex lens. There is an erect one from the front

surface and an inverted one from the back surface. The smaller the radius of curvature of the surface the smaller and brighter will the image be.

Now hold the candle at one side of the subject's eye—from the other side observe the images of the candle: (1) from the anterior surface of the cornea—easily seen, erect and bright; (2) from the anterior surface of the lens—erect, larger, not so bright, coming from nearer the centre of the pupil; (3) from the posterior surface of the lens—small, inverted, and not easily seen. Ask the subject to look at the far wall, then while observing the images ask him to look at your finger held near the eye. Image (2) will be seen to move closer to (1), becoming at the same time smaller and brighter. During accommodation, then, the lens becomes more convex by the bulging forward of its anterior surface. Draw a diagram to illustrate the reflecting surfaces and the light pathways.

If a phakoscope is available Sanson's images can be more readily observed. The method will be demonstrated.

Scheiner's Experiment.

(73) Make two pin holes in a card about 1 to 2 mm. apart (less than the diameter of the pupil). Place the card close to one eye, the other being closed, and look through the holes at a distant object—e.g. the cross-piece of a window. Hold a pencil with its point about 10 in. in front of the eye so that it comes into the field of vision. While looking at the distant object the pencil point will appear double; carefully slide along an opaque card to cover one only of the pin holes, and notice which of the double images of the pencil disappears. Uncover the pin holes and focus on to the pencil point; the window cross-piece will now appear double. Again slide in a card to obscure the same pin hole as before, and notice which of the double images disappears.

Draw diagrams for each case to show the paths of rays from the two objects to the retina.

Localisation.

(74) The apparatus consists of a vertical stand painted dull black, with a small horizontal window. Two white diverging lines are painted on a black background on a drum behind the window; by rotating the drum one can vary the distance between the two short white lines exposed through the window. The window is

flood-lit by a small lamp; connect the wires to the C terminals (accumulator).

With chalk and string make as large a semi-circle as possible on the bench. The subject places one eye just above bench level at the centre of the semi-circle and looks steadily at a fixed point, a piece of white chalk, placed on the semi-circle opposite. The other eye must be kept closed.

Starting with the lines close together the experimenter moves the stand around the semi-circle from the fixation point until the subject (still fixing the chalk) says he can no longer distinguish the two lines.

The lines are moved farther apart by rotating the drum a little, and the stand is moved farther out until the lines cease to give rise to a double sensation. Repeat the procedure until the lines are at their maximum distance apart.

At each position at which the white lines just cease to be seen separately measure the distance between the two lines on the drum; divide this value by the radius of the semi-circle on the bench. The angle between the lines, A, will be found on looking up this value in table of natural sines or tans. The angle B between the chalk at the fixation point and the centre of the drum can be measured similarly or by means of a protractor. Plot the value of A on the ordinate against the value of B on the abscissa.

Field of Vision.

(75) The charting of the field of vision is often of great practical value in the localisation of lesions in the brain.

(1) For clinical purposes here is a simple procedure which may discover gross changes. The subject stands facing the examiner, with his back to the light and at a distance of about 2 ft. Each eye must be examined separately, while one is being tested the other should be closed. The examiner closes the eye opposite the subject's closed eye. The subject should look fixedly at the examiner's open eye, while the latter, holding his hand midway between himself and the subject, moves the outstretched forefinger from the periphery towards the centre of the visual field. The subject is asked to say when he sees the movement of the finger. Both the examiner and the subject should see the movement of the finger at the same moment provided that in both the field of vision is normal. The movements of the hand are repeated in different meridians of the field until it has all been explored. Thus the

examiner's field is compared with the subject's, and as the examiner is constantly watching the subject's eye any wandering from the point of fixation is quickly observed and corrected.

(2) A more accurate examination can be made by the peri-meter. This consists of a metal quadrant rotatable about one end so as to describe a hemisphere; the fixed end is mounted on a stand in front of a large black disc. At the centre of the black disc there is a small white disc or a small plane mirror used as a point of fixation. The quadrant is marked off in degrees so that the position of the rider on it can be read off. Behind the black disc is a frame to carry the perimeter chart which rotates with the quadrant. At the opposite end of the instrument is an adjustable chin-rest on a pillar. The subject places his chin on this and the height is adjusted till the eye to be examined is on the same level as the fixation point and is directly above the forked end of the pillar. The subject should sit with his back to the light and close the other eye or have it covered with a shade.

Make a large pin hole through the centre of the appropriate perimeter chart (right or left) and put it vertically in the frame while the quadrant is horizontal (at three o'clock to the subject). Bring up the hinged shelf engraved in degrees against the chart. The position of the shelf now indicates on the chart the position of the quadrant with respect to the subject.

Cover the disc on the rider with white chalk and take it to the end of the quadrant, bring the rider inwards until it just comes within the field of vision of the eye of the subject who is gazing steadily at the fixation point. Read off the angle on the quadrant, lay a pencil point on the shelf at the position indicating this angle and push against the chart. Repeat this procedure with different positions of the quadrant. Finally join up the dots on the chart to get the boundary of the field of vision and compare with the field already printed on it. Try to account for the peculiar shape of the field.

The perimeter may, of course, be used to map out the blind spot by bringing the rider along the quadrant in several meridians close to the horizontal on the temporal side of the field.

(3) If the perimeter is not available the horizontal and vertical limits of the field of vision can be mapped out by chalking semi-circles on the bench and on a vertical blackboard. The subject places his eye at the centre of the semi-circle (which is placed at

Map normal for each eye

    Red " " "

    Green " " "

    Blue. for one eye

    Yellow " the same eye

To map colour fields mark where colour disappears while you can still perceive the object.

—— you also have coloured riders

— in the appropriate colour

    Read also the preceding paragraph. p. 110.

H

the edge of the bench or blackboard) and gazes steadily at a piece of chalk on the circumference opposite him.

The observer uses the dull black-painted stand (used in the localisation experiment, p. 108) to find the limit of the field of vision. A black card with a central white spot is placed in the holder so that it is flood-lit by the lamp. Connect the flex to the C terminals. The apparatus is brought from the periphery of the field of vision along the semi-circle towards the fixation point. When the subject sees the white spot a chalk mark is made. The procedure is repeated from the other end of the semi-circle.

The Fundus Oculi.

(76) This work will be done in the optical room.

The use of the ophthalmoscope, both the older reflecting pattern and the newer electrical pattern, will be demonstrated. Afterwards try to use each type on a. model eyes (microscope eye-pieces), b. eye of the rabbit (atropinised), and c. on the human eye.

The indirect method is rather difficult and there is not sufficient time to practise it at this meeting, so that only the direct method will be attempted; the following notes refer to it alone and are supplementary to the remarks of the demonstrator.

Both subject and observer must relax their accommodation by "looking into the distance" in spite of the fact that the object looked at is only a few inches away. Both must remove spectacles if these are worn. Use the right eye to look at the subject's right eye, and left eye to look at his left eye. Begin about a foot or two away from the subject, and while looking through the eyehole move the ophthalmoscope about (but steadying it against the bridge of the nose) till a red reflex is obtained from the pupil. Gradually decrease the distance until the fundus is seen. It may help at first to put up a weak minus (i.e. concave) lens at the eye-hole of the ophthalmoscope. This has the effect of neutralising your accommodation which you may have difficulty at first in relaxing. This difficulty disappears after a little practice.

If either the subject or the observer wears glasses then it will be necessary to put up a lens of approximately the same value as the correction. Every student who wears glasses should know his correction and should keep the prescription.

Practise first with the model eyes; describe what is seen—is the image erect or inverted? Then examine the rabbit's eye. Then examine a human eye. Sketch what is seen—ask the subject to

look up and down and to the side so that as much of the fundus as possible is seen.

If two members of each section will volunteer to allow homatropine drops (1 per cent.) to be put into one eye about half an hour before the examination this will allow everyone to have a good view of the fundus. The effect can be counteracted afterwards by instilling 1 per cent. eserine. What are the actions of atropine or homatropine and of eserine?

Put up a plus 20 lens in the ophthalmoscope: the corneal surface is now easily seen. A plus 12 will enable the anterior surface, and a plus 8 the posterior surface of the lens to be focused.

Retinal Vessels.

(77) The subject stands with one shoulder against the wall of the dark room and looks along the wall. By means of a candle and a convex lens a bright light is projected on to his sclerotic. He will see branching shadows (Purkinje's images) on the wall. These are the shadows of the retinal vessels projected, as are all visual phenomena, on the exterior. Draw a diagram to illustrate this experiment.

(78) Look at the sky through a pin hole in a piece of black paper held close to the eye. Close the other eye. Move the paper up and down and from side to side. Shadows of the retinal vessels will be seen—the group of blood vessels seen depends on the direction of movement. The vessels lie in front of the retina, and in this experiment a clear-cut shadow is cast by the light from the small aperture on to the sensitive layer of the retina. When the paper is held stationary the vessels are not seen because the retina becomes adapted. This accounts for the fact that the vessels are not seen in normal circumstances. Also light usually enters the eye from the whole of the lens uncovered by the iris, and therefore light is passing any one retinal vessel at various angles to reach the rods and cones. Only a diffuse shadow of a vessel can in these circumstances be cast on the light-sensitive layer.

Colour Vision.

(79) The large colour discs (red, green, yellow, etc.) are provided with radial slits. They can be overlapped to any desired angle, thus enabling varying sectors of different colours to be displayed. Use first red, green, and blue discs; rotate them rapidly in the colour mixer. By varying the amount of each colour a large

range of colour sensations can be produced, including a neutral grey. It is not possible to produce a sensation of white with this apparatus, presumably because of difficulty in getting discs of the proper colours. If complementary colours, e.g. blue and yellow, are rotated together in the correct proportions a neutral grey is obtained.

Rotate the special disc (one half black, the other half white with a few concentric marks) at first very slowly and then faster. Various colour sensations will be produced in spite of the fact that the disc has only black and white markings.

(80) *Tests for colour blindness.*—The subject is given a box of bundles of wools of various colours (Holmgren's wools). Pick one out and ask him to select all the other bundles of the same hue. This test often fails to detect colour blindness. Edridge-Green's or Ishihara's book of tests is more useful in practice. The instructions and key should be read. These books contain a series of plates all with splashes of colour in the same irregular pattern, but the colours differ from plate to plate. In the pattern letters are formed in splashes of one colour on a background of splashes of a different colour. The subject is asked to name the letters or figures so picked out.

(81) Edridge-Green's colour lantern is used to test engine-drivers, aviators, and sailors. It is so arranged that different colours at varying apertures can be shown—these represent railway signals and navigation lights at varying distances. There is also a series of modifying glasses by which the effect of fog, etc., on the colour of signals can be imitated.

(82) *Field of vision for colours.*—Estimate the field of vision for white, green, red, yellow and blue by the method already described (p. 112), using matt black cards with coloured circles. The sensation must be more than a mere awareness of something in the visual field. Move the stand in from the periphery until the subject is certain he can distinguish the colour.

After-Images.

(83) These three experiments are performed in the optical room.

1. Gaze fixedly at a bright circle of light (opal electric bulb) for 20 seconds. Turn off the light and look at the black surface of the wall. A positive after-image, owing to the absence of a second stimulus, will be seen.

2. Again gaze fixedly at the light for 20 seconds, then quickly look at the centre of a large white area. Owing to the second stimulus (the white area) the after-image will now be negative, and will appear as a dark area on the white ground. Note that the after-image is always of the same shape and size as the original stimulus.

3. Look steadily at the piece of red glass which is illuminated from behind. Then look at a white area. Again there will be a negative after-image, in this case green, which is the complementary colour. Repeat with blue, etc.

(**84**) *Bidwell's experiment.*—This shows that an after-image can, under special circumstances, cause suppression of the primary image. A paper of some bright colour, e.g. red or yellow, is placed in a clip attached to the standard of the colour mixer. Mount Bidwell's disc on the axis of the colour mixer. This is a circular card from which a 60° sector has been cut. One half of the remainder is painted black, the other is white. When the missing sector is in such a position that the coloured paper is seen, then the latter should fill up the whole of the space, but it should not project beyond the circumference of the disc. Rotate the disc about seven times a second so that the open sector, the white sector and then the black sector pass in that order in front of the coloured paper. Keep the eye fixed on a point in the centre of the coloured paper; as the disc is rotated in front of it the original colour will be lost and the complementary colour will take its place. This is due to the fact that the negative after-image, which follows when the white sector replaces the original colour stimulus, persists for some time longer than the primary response, viz. until the disc, if rotated at the correct speed, has made one complete revolution. The next appearance of the original colour is suppressed by this persisting after-image, but itself gives rise to another after-image, similar to the first, when the white sector again comes in front of the eyes. Thus, although the primary stimulus impresses itself on the retina at each revolution of the disc, one appreciates only a succession of fused negative after-images. If the effect is not noticed immediately, vary the speed of rotation.

Flicker.

(**85**) Rotate the flicker disc; this is marked with alternate black and white rectangles set on concentric circles. Look at a point near the circumference. As the speed of rotation increases, the

flickering sensation ceases, giving way to an even grey sensation. At this speed the inner rectangles, which are the same size as the outer rectangles, will still flicker. Shine a bright light on the disc. Does this affect the speed at which fusion occurs?

Visual Acuity.

(86) Visual acuity is tested by Snellen's types. A card on which are printed rows of letters of different sizes is viewed in a good light from a distance of exactly 6 metres. Below each row is a number indicating the distance in metres at which that row can be read by a person with normal vision. This is the distance at which the width of the black strokes forming the letters subtends at the eye an angle of one minute, and the whole letter subtends an angle of five minutes.

From 6 metres, using one eye at a time, read off the letters on the card, beginning at the top. Note the number below the last row that can be read. The visual acuity V is expressed as 6 over this number; normal vision is therefore 6/6. Three motor-car numbers are also shown; the middle one corresponds in size, when viewed at 6 metres, to a motor-car number at 25 yards (Road Traffic Act, 1935).

Lessened visual acuity may be due to (1) defect in the nervous apparatus—i.e. retina, nerve or brain; (2) defect in the media of the eye—e.g. cornea or lens; (3) ametropia, or to a combination of these. To show that lessened visual acuity is due simply to (3) and not to something more serious, the principle of the pin hole camera can be applied. Make a pin hole in a piece of black paper. If you have bad visual acuity remove your spectacles, if you have good acuity put up a lens (spectacles borrowed from a colleague) to disturb it; look through the pin hole held close to the eye, when brightly lit objects will be clearly seen in the absence of defects (1) and (2) above.

Astigmatism.

(87) The card is also provided with a set of radiating lines. Look at them with one eye at a time. Do all the lines appear equally black? If some appear grey then the defect astigmatism exists.

If glasses are worn give the results of these tests with and without glasses.

(88) *Clark's model* consists of a lamp illuminating a Maltese cross, and three lenses all of the same focal length, *a.* spherical convex,

b. cylindrical convex (axis vertical), *c.* cylindrical convex (axis horizontal). The images of the cross formed by *a.*, *b.*, and *c.* are seen on the ground-glass screen. That formed by *a.* is unobjectionable, but those formed by *b.* and *c.* are merely vertical and horizontal bars with a diffuse light around them. This is a gross case of astigmatism, i.e. each point of the object is not represented by a single point on the image; it is due, of course, to the fact that the refractive power of the cylindrical lenses is greater in one direction than in any other. If the astigmatism is regular as in this instance it can easily be corrected by an appropriate cylindrical lens. Slide *b.* over *c.* The image is now as good as with *a.*

(**89**) *Placido's disc.*—Stand facing a good light and look through the central aperture of Placido's disc at the subject's eye. A convex lens in the aperture magnifies the reflection from the cornea of the black and white concentric circles of the disc. If the cornea is spherical the rings will be regular and truly circular. Regular astigmatism will cause the rings to be oval in shape though still concentric. Irregular astigmatism, conical cornea, etc., will distort the rings in various ways.

Myopia and Hypermetropia.

(**90**) Kühne's artificial eye consists simply of a convex lens behind which is a movable ground-glass screen to represent the retina. Place a candle in front of the eye and move the screen till the image is sharply focused. This will represent the condition of emmetropia. Now push the screen forward nearer the lens. The anteroposterior measurement of the eye is now too short and the image of the candle is poor. If now a suitable convex lens is placed in front of the eye lens the image is once more accurate. The same result could be brought about in the living eye by accommodation —the lens then becomes more convex and so a good image is formed. This shortness of the eyeball is the most common cause of hypermetropia or longsightedness. If the object, the candle in this instance, is brought too near the eye, then accommodation is not sufficient to bring the image to a sharp focus on the retina. That is to say, that the near point may be at a considerable distance from the eye and objects close at hand cannot be seen clearly unless, as in this experiment, a convex lens is put in front of the eye.

Now push back the screen so that the "eye" is too long, the condition usually found in myopia. The image will be poor

unless (1) the candle is brought nearer to the eye (hence the usual name shortsightedness), or (2) a concave or minus lens is placed in front of the eye.

Return to the position of the emmetropic eye. Now push the candle nearer the eye, the image deteriorates. This is very nearly the state of affairs in presbyopia, where the lens has lost its elasticity and accommodation cannot occur. What kind of lens will have to be given to an old person who finds he has to hold his book at an uncomfortable distance for reading?

The External Eye Muscles.

(91) Revise the anatomy of the orbit, including the nerve supply of the muscles. Examine the skull which has been cut horizontally through the orbits. Note that the orbit looks forward and outward, whereas the optical axis (the anteroposterior line of the eye) when the eyes are looking straight ahead at a distant object is directly anteroposterior. It is the angular discrepancy between these two axes which gives rise to the inward movements produced by the contraction of the superior and inferior recti, in addition to the upward and downward movements. The external and internal recti have simple rotatory actions—they move the globe so that the pupil looks out or in towards the nose. Both of the oblique muscles pull from the anterior and medial aspect of the orbit and their tendons pass over the equator of the eyeball and are inserted behind it. Obviously, then, when the superior oblique contracts it will pull up the posterior surface of the globe and so the pupil will move down, and also out, because of the relationship of the direction of pull to the visual axis.

This summary of the movements produced by the muscles will be made more clear by the use of the model eye. Make a diagram on the bench to represent a horizontal section of the skull through the orbits. Place the wooden model eye in its position in the diagram. Pass knitting-pins through the holes to indicate the axes for rotation of the eyeball when (1) interior and exterior recti, (2) superior and inferior recti, and (3) superior and inferior oblique contract. Rotate the model eye and watch the movements of the pupil. Make a table indicating the action of each muscle and its nerve supply.

Double Vision.

(92) Normally double vision does not occur because the muscles

acting through their controlling mechanism arrange that images of external objects fall on corresponding points of the retinae. Draw a diagram to explain corresponding points. Look straight forward, press gently with a finger on the upper eyelid, double vision will result. It is possible, however, to produce double vision when the two eyes are allowed to move freely. Look at a pencil held up before the eyes, the window bars seen indistinctly in the background will appear double; by looking at the window bars the pencil will appear double. Draw diagrams to explain this.

(**93**) Any serious defect of the neuromuscular system of the eyes will give rise to a squint and produce diplopia unless the squinting eye has become blind or the image it receives does not reach consciousness. Why is there not necessarily double vision in paralysis of the third cranial nerve?

(**94**) A latent defect of neuromuscular co-ordination can be made apparent by any method which makes the two fields of vision so dissimilar that no fusion is called for. The Maddox rod consists of a red glass with a corrugated surface. Put on the test frame and put the glass in front of one eye while looking at a bright light. The covered eye will see a bright red streak the direction of which depends on the axis of the corrugations. Does the streak pass through the light or to one side? What does this indicate?

(**95**) Make a series of figures from 1–10 across the page of your book with an arrow about half an inch below the 5 and pointing up to it; look at this diagram at a distance of 10 in. through the spectacles, which have discs of metal instead of lenses. The discs have narrow horizontal slits which are continued into narrow tunnels. Move the head about until by testing (by closing the eyes alternately) only the row of figures is seen through one slit and only the arrow through the other slit. Read off the position of the arrow with both eyes open; afterwards enter a dotted arrow there. Does this correspond to the actual position of the arrow? If not, what does this indicate?

Binocular Field of Vision.

(**96**) Draw as large a semi-circle as possible on the top of the bench. Put the bridge of the nose at the centre and place a piece of white chalk on the circle opposite to act as the fixation point. Using the method previously described (p. 112) find the field

I

of vision of the right eye, then the left eye, and then of both together; keep the head in the same position throughout. Measure the angles and make a diagram. What advantage of binocular vision is shown by this experiment? Bring the fixation point (i.e. the piece of chalk) nearer the nose so that it is about 1 in. farther away than the near point. Make a circle of this radius and proceed as before. Compare with the previous result.

Stereoscopic Vision.

(**97**) Thread a needle; note how you do it and how long it takes. Close one eye and repeat the experiment. How does this affect your performance?

(**98**) Hold one of the wooden blocks provided about 10 in. in front of the eyes. Describe its appearance as seen by the right eye alone, and then by the left eye alone. Show that two slightly different views of an object can be fused to give an impression of solidity when they are combined with the help of a stereoscope— either Wheatstone's or Brewster's. Draw sketches to indicate the paths of the light rays when using these stereoscopes.

(**99**) An X-ray photograph is really a shadow photograph and gives no information about the relative position of the various structures. Before the operative removal of foreign bodies, such as bullets, accurate localisation is possible by combining in a stereoscope two skiagrams taken from slightly different positions. A modified Wheatstone apparatus for trans-illumination of X-ray negatives is available. Move the films about in their holders until a stereoscopic effect is obtained. Give a diagram of the apparatus and explain the appearances.

CHAPTER SEVEN

CIRCULATION IN MAN

Cardiac Sounds.

(**100**) THERE will be a demonstration by means of a microphone, with valve amplifier and loudspeaker, of the heart sounds. It will be found easier to appreciate the general character and the rhythm of the sounds in this way before attempting to use the stethoscope.

After the demonstration listen with the bell of the stethoscope at the region of the apex impulse in the fifth interspace about $3\frac{1}{2}$ in. from the mid-line, where the first sound is best heard, and also at the junction of the second right costal cartilage with the sternum, where the second (aortic) sound is best heard. The second pulmonic sound is best heard in the second left interspace close to the sternum. In children and adolescents the second pulmonic sound is louder than the second aortic sound.

Cardiac Movements.

(**101**) The shape and movements of the human heart will be demonstrated on the X-ray screen. Note the movements of the auricles and the ventricles. Revise your knowledge of the anatomy of the human heart, paying particular attention to the position of the line dividing auricles and ventricles and the position of the aorta.

The Pulse.

(**102**) The subject should be sitting at rest for some minutes so that any disturbance due to activity or emotion may pass off. Palpate the radial artery at the wrist with the tips of the fingers.

    1. *Rate.*—Count the number of beats during one minute.

    2. *Rhythm.*—Do the pulsations follow at regular intervals, i.e. is the rhythm regular? In some students it may be found that the heart rate increases slightly during inspiration—sinus arrhythmia. Are all the pulsations of equal force?

    3. *Volume.*—The volume or amplitude of expansion of the

artery can be noted by light palpation; estimate it as large, medium or small.

4. *Form.*—Try to appreciate the normal rise, maintenance, and fall of the wave in the artery. Compare the mental impression with the graphic record obtained later.

5. *Force and tension.*—To determine the systolic blood pressure (force) three fingers are placed on the radial artery. Firm pressure is made with the distal finger to prevent any pulsation reaching the middle finger from the palmar arch. The proximal finger then gradually compresses the pulse till it can no longer be felt by the middle finger. This gives a very rough approximation to systolic pressure.

An idea of the diastolic pressure or tension may be obtained by estimating the pressure required to flatten the vessel between beats. If the tension is low, light pressure will be sufficient to flatten the vessel, but considerable pressure will be required if the tension is high.

It must be emphasised that, although these two palpation methods can be and often are valuable, a quantitatively reliable estimate of the blood pressure can be made only by means of the sphygmomanometer.

6. *State of the vessel wall.*—Empty the artery by pressure with the finger, and then palpate it longitudinally and laterally. The healthy vessel is impalpable, or felt only with difficulty.

(**103**) *Dudgeon's sphygmograph.*—Smoke the kymograph drum; remove the paper and cut it transversely into strips (6 in. × 1 in.) by

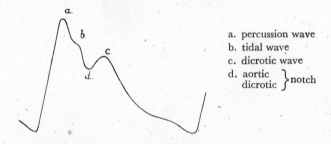

a. percussion wave
b. tidal wave
c. dicrotic wave
d. aortic } notch
   dicrotic }

means of the guillotine provided with a check bar 1 in. from the edge of the base plate. Great care must be taken to cut the strips exactly to this size and to make the edges parallel. Wind up the clockwork motor of the sphygmograph gently by means of the knurled screw; it can be started and stopped by the little lever on

the top of the case. Insert a strip of smoked paper between the fluted roller (below) and the two wheels (above). Mark the position of the subject's radial artery with ink. Lay his forearm on a support a few inches above the bench level so that the wrist can be flexed or extended by him as required. Rest the spring button of the apparatus on the artery—keep the clockwork casing proximal. Do not strap the instrument to the wrist, but apply it with varying pressure in various positions of the wrist and at various settings of the eccentric pressing on the spring button till the maximum excursion of the writing point is obtained. Then allow the motor to drive the paper through the apparatus. Label the waves on the traces, also make a note of the pulse rate on the trace.

Blood Pressure in Man.

(104) The sphygmomanometer consists of a valved pump and a rubber armlet which is connected to some kind of manometer. The best type of manometer is a glass U-tube containing mercury. If the two limbs are of the same diameter then the scale is short as in the original Riva-Rocci apparatus. But if one limb is made very wide then the scale is very much longer (nearly double)— this is illustrated by the Baumanometer. Some patterns, e.g. Tycos, have an aneroid manometer, which must be standardised against a mercury manometer. Have the subject sitting at rest with the muscles relaxed. It is essential that there should be no emotional or muscular disturbance, as this may make quite considerable alterations in the readings.

The subject's upper arm is bared to the shoulder. The centre of the completely deflated rubber bag is placed over the line of the brachial artery—the lower edge must be kept 1 in. above the bend of the elbow. Wrap the cloth bag which covers the rubber bag round and round the arm and tuck in (do not tie) the end under one of the turns. The antecubital fossa must be left bare. Put the manometer in such a position that it can readily be seen by the observer but not by the subject. Make sure that the level of the mercury is at zero on the scale. The box must be on a level table and the scale should be read when the observer's eye is at the same height as the mercury column.

Palpation method.—Palpate the subject's radial artery with the tips of the index and middle fingers of the left hand. Screw down the escape valve which is placed just above the bulb of the pump.

Pump up the armlet rapidly (to about 150 mm.) till the pulse disappears, then let out the air very slowly by unscrewing the valve a very little. Watch the manometer and note the reading on it when the pulse returns—this is the systolic blood pressure or S.B.P. Allow the pressure to fall rapidly once a reading is obtained.

Do not keep up the constriction any longer than is necessary; between readings let the pressure down to zero and allow the arm circulation to return to normal. This advice applies also to the next method.

Auscultation method.—This is the only reliable method for estimation of diastolic blood pressure (D.B.P.). It will be demonstrated by means of a microphone and loudspeaker. Palpate the brachial artery on the medial side of the biceps tendon. Hold the bell of the stethoscope with the left hand lightly over the site of maximal pulsation but not in contact with the cuff, and blow up the armlet to about 30 mm. Hg. above S.B.P. Let the pressure down *slowly*. Above S.B.P. no sounds are heard. At S.B.P. successive tapping sounds are heard; note the reading on the manometer at their first appearance. This reading of the S.B.P. may be a few millimetres higher than that obtained by palpation. As the pressure is slowly decreased the sounds increase to their maximum intensity and then decrease at first gradually and later suddenly and soon disappear. The point where the loud clear sounds change abruptly to the dull and muffled sounds should be taken as the diastolic pressure. Sometimes at D.B.P. the taps disappear quite suddenly without any muffled sounds being heard.

If the method of palpation is used before the auscultatory method the unusual case with a silent gap will not be missed. In these cases after the first sounds have been heard there is an auscultatory gap below which the sounds reappear. This silent gap is not very uncommon in cases of aortic disease and high blood pressure.

On listening with a stethoscope an attempt must be made—it becomes easy with practice—to discard mentally all sounds other than those being investigated. It will be found that the taps are heard a fraction of a second before the mercury in the manometer bobs up a little. (The movement of the mercury is just a little late because of its inertia.) Sounds occurring in between beats can be disregarded. Record the readings and the pulse pressure,

i.e. S.B.P. minus D.B.P. What is the rationale of the two methods?

The Effect of Vasodilatation on Blood Pressure.

(105) Anyone who has had any "heart trouble" must not act as subject in this experiment. Make a rough table with three columns on a sheet of paper for Time, S.B.P., and D.B.P. Record normal blood pressure over three consecutive minutes. Then ask the subject to inhale deeply through a piece of cotton wool on which two drops of amyl nitrite have been placed. Record the behaviour of S.B.P. and D.B.P. at minute intervals (or every two minutes if this is too difficult) and continue to take readings for several minutes after normal B.P. has been reached. While the observations are being made any marked alteration in pulse rate can be heard and noted without being counted. (If a second observer happens to be available he should count the pulse rate for half a minute at minute intervals.) Watch also the skin colour and the respiration of the subject. When the experiment is over ask the subject to describe his sensations after inhalation of the drug. Draw a graph: abscissa 1 in. = 5 mins.; ordinate 1 in. = 20 mm. Hg.

The Venous Flow.

(106) Tie a handkerchief around the subject's arm just above the elbow and observe the appearance of the veins in the forearm. Note the occurrence of little swellings on the course of the veins, showing the position of the valves.

Place a finger (A) on one of the veins and note the position of the valve (V) next above it. With another finger press the blood in the vein towards the upper arm, keeping the finger (A) in the same position. There will be no influx of blood from above and the portion of the vein between the finger A and the valve V will remain collapsed. The vein above V will be distended and the valve will show clearly. Still keeping finger A in the same position place another finger above the valve V and attempt to press the blood towards the wrist. The blood cannot be forced through unless pressure sufficient to rupture the valve is used. Remove finger A and note that the vein which was before emptied is immediately filled from below. These are some of Harvey's original experiments. Can you recall any other evidence for the circulation of the blood? (Do *not* write it in your book.) What is the function of the valves in the veins?

The Venous Pulse.

(**107**) The variations of pressure in the right auricle are transmitted to the great veins. Hence information about the auricular function can be got from a trace of the pressure in the veins. A metal cup with a flattened side is placed above the clavicle just lateral to the sternal head of the right sternomastoid muscle when the subject is in the supine position with the shoulders supported by a small pillow. The outlet tube from the cup is connected by a rubber tube to a tambour the writing point of which is made to write lightly on a lightly smoked drum. The metal cup is moved about till the maximum jugular pulse is obtained. By palpation of the left carotid artery during the recording of the trace it will be possible to determine which of the waves is the "c" wave; the wave before this will be the "a" wave, and the wave after it will be the "v" wave. For clinical purposes it is usual to record the radial pulse simultaneously with the jugular pulse in order to determine which wave is the "c" wave. The "c" wave begins about 1/10 sec. before the beginning of the radial wave.

Describe the trace obtained and give the causes of the variations of the jugular pressure (a, c and v waves) throughout a cardiac cycle.

Venous Pressure.

(**108**) The subject allows his arm to hang vertically downwards. The veins of the arm will become distended. The observer slowly raises the subject's arm till the veins above the wrist begin to empty. Measure the vertical height between the wrist and the third costal cartilage at its sternal end, i.e. the level of entry of the superior vena cava. How would you express the pressure in the auricle at this point?

The pressure in the superficial veins can be measured by a method similar to that used for determining arterial pressure. A flat glass cup is stuck down on to the skin of the forearm over a vein by means of collodion. When the collodion is dry connect the outlet tube from the cup to the water manometer and rubber bellows. Increase the pressure in the system till the vein is just made to empty; the reading of the water manometer at this point gives the pressure in the vein. Assuming that there is a continuous blood column up to the heart from the part of the vein covered by the cup, again calculate the pressure in the auricle at the point of entry of the superior vena cava.

Strength of Capillaries.

(**109**) Mark a circle of 6 cm. diameter with its centre at the centre of the antecubital fossa. Inspect the area inside the circle for capillary haemorrhages (petechiae). If a doubtful marking fades on pressure applied by means of a piece of plane glass (microscope slide or glass tongue spatula) it is not a petechia. Mark any petechiae found with ink. Seat the subject at a table with his elbows resting on it. Wrap a sphygmomanometer armlet round the arm at least 2·5 cm. above the marked circle. Pump up the armlet to 50 mm. Hg. and maintain this pressure for 15 minutes. On releasing the pressure count the petechiae in the circle. A very good light is essential for inspection as the petechiae are very small.

About 90 per cent. of people show less than eight petechiae. The number of petechiae is increased near the menstrual period; deficiency of vitamin C may produce a large number of petechiae. There are other unknown causes of increased capillary fragility.

Response of Skin Capillaries to Injury.

(**110**) Draw a blunt-ended instrument, e.g. a closed forceps, firmly across the volar surface of the forearm. The reaction varies with the amount of the injury done to the skin. Moderate pressure will obviously only displace the blood from the skin locally. The reaction varies from person to person, but when fully developed it consists of (Lewis):

1. A red line (*tache*) in the track of the instrument.
2. A surrounding ill-defined area or *flare*.
3. A local oedema or even a wheal developing under the track of the instrument (*dermatograph*).

Lewis suggests that a histamine-like substance is liberated in the skin on injury, and it is the cause of this triple response. Compare the appearances noted above with the reaction of the skin capillaries to histamine and adrenaline. Wash the forearm with soap and water, dry, and clean with spirit on a piece of cotton wool. On the skin place drops one inch apart in this order from above downwards:

1. Ringer's fluid.   2. 1 in 10,000 histamine.
3. 1 in 1000 adrenaline.

Flame a needle and scratch through 1 firmly but not to the

K

effusion of blood. Flame the needle again and scratch through 2. Flame and scratch through 3.

Explain the occurrence of the oedema. Discuss briefly its possible relation to " shock."

Describe the reaction to adrenaline, look for cutis anserina (goose skin), and explain the appearances, related if possible to the nerve supply of the structures involved.

CHAPTER EIGHT

RESPIRATION

Changes in the Chest Wall.

(**111**) USING the tailor's tape, measure the circumference of the chest in full inspiration and in full expiration at the axillary level as high up as possible and also at the level of the sternal end of the sixth costal cartilage. What is the physiological significance of the figure for chest expansion?

(**112**) Use the cyrtometer to find the actual shape of the chest in the same four positions. This instrument consists of two pieces of lead-covered electric cable united by a piece of rubber tubing to form a hinge. The hinge is applied directly over the spinous processes and held firmly in position. The two pieces of cable are then brought round the sides and moulded accurately to the contour of the chest wall. They are crossed in front; the mid-line of the sternum is marked on each by sliding rubber bands along to that position. The joint allows the cyrtometer to be removed without destroying the "set"; it is adjusted on a large sheet of brown paper and the outline traced. Superimpose the four traces on one another, keeping the hinge over the same point of the paper on each occasion.

(In the case of women students the chest measurements should be made below the mammary glands with both arms laterally extended at shoulder level.)

(**113**) An X-ray demonstration will show the respiratory movements more clearly. The upper border of the liver shadow defines the position of the diaphragm so that its movements are easily followed. Make a note of (1) the most actively moving parts, (2) the amount of movement seen on the fluorescent screen in normal and very deep breathing. Note also the alteration in density of the lung fields on inspiration. The movements of the ribs are not so easy to follow unless one concentrates on a single rib and follows it through the respiratory cycle.

(114) The demonstrator will percuss out the liver dullness in inspiration and expiration. Find how far the movement of the liver shadow on the screen agrees with the shifting of the dullness.

(115) By means of a microphone and loudspeaker the sounds caused by passage of air in and out of the chest will be demonstrated. Listen with a stethoscope over the trachea for bronchial breathing and in the axilla for vesicular breathing and try to appreciate the differences between the two as described by the demonstrator.

Tidal Air.

(116) This is the air passing in or out of the lungs at each respiration. Sterilise the rubber mouthpiece in an antiseptic solution and wash it. Close the nose with a clip. Place the rubber mouthpiece in the mouth and breathe through the valves attached to it. Note which valve allows air to escape on expiration—connect this to the spirometer.

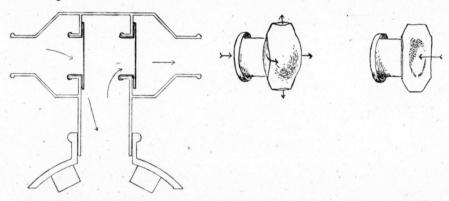

The diagram on the left shows the mouthpiece and valve housing and the path of the air to the spirometer which is connected by a wide bore rubber pipe to the right-hand tube of the housing   The two small sketches on the right indicate how the rubber valves behave according to the direction of the air stream.

The spirometer is simply a counterpoised gas holder. A writing point fixed to the counterpoise weight is made to write on a slowly revolving drum. Breathe quietly in and out. Each expiration will be recorded in the drum. Take the average of several records, and calculate the volume of expired air given that 1 mm. means 20 c.c. volume. This result multiplied by the number of breaths per minute is equal to the ventilation for one minute.

Complemental Air.

(117) This is the additional air which can be drawn in after a normal inspiration, thus expanding the lungs into the complemental pleura.

Sterilise a glass mouthpiece and rinse in tap water. Fit it to the rubber tubing of the spirometer. Raise the bell of the spirometer so that it is full of air. After a normal inspiration hold the nose and see how much air can be sucked out of the spirometer.

Supplemental Air.

(118) This is the extra air which can be forced out after a normal expiration, and can be determined by simple reversal of all the instructions for the measurement of complemental air.

Vital Capacity.

(119) Sterilise a glass mouthpiece and then rinse it in tap water. Fit the mouthpiece to the tubing of the spirometer. Take the reading on the scale. Expire and inspire as fully as possible, then expire as deeply as possible into the spirometer. This is the maximum amount of air which can be moved in and out of the respiratory passages. See if your previous determinations of tidal, supplemental and complemental air add up to give the vital capacity.

Minimum figures for vital capacity are given by the R.A.F. in their tests of fitness for flying. How does the value you obtain compare with this?

Flack's Air Force Manometer Test (40 mm. Test).

(120) After a full expiration and a full inspiration apply the mouth to the mouthpiece (sterilised as above) of the mercury manometer and raise the column to a height of 40 mm. (i.e. 20 mm. up on one side and 20 mm. down on the other) by a steadily exerted expiration; hold it at this height and note the time to "breaking point." The hand may be used to support the muscles of the face and mouth. Flack's standard for R.A.F. pilots is 52 seconds.

Recording of Respiratory Movements.

(121) The stethograph consists of a piece of corrugated hose-pipe with a stopper at each end and an air outlet to the recording tambour. Tie the stethograph round the part of the chest showing the maximum respiratory excursion, and adjust the amount of

air in the recording system by blowing in or sucking air out of the side tube so that at the mean position between inspiration and expiration the diaphragm of the tambour is flat. Have the subject sitting with his back to the drum and record the movements during quiet respiration on a slow drum (about 1 in. to each respiration). Run a time-trace and annotate the curves. Discuss the information given by the trace.

Record the effect of swallowing; the subject takes a mouthful of water and holds it in his mouth without swallowing, take a record of normal respirations while the subject breathes through his nose. At the command "swallow" put a stroke on the drum below the trace.

Record also the effect of talking; the effect is best seen if the subject recites, e.g., a speech from Shakespeare. Fill in below the trace the words of the speech.

The Influence of Carbon Dioxide on Respiration.

(122) Use the stethograph as above, but record on a very slow drum (about five respirations per inch). The subject must not be allowed to see the drum at any time.

1. Take a trace of, say, six normal respirations; while the drum is still running, the subject, at the order of the observer, holds his nostrils and stops breathing; after a time it will be impossible for the subject to hold the breath any longer; continue to record respirations till they return to normal. The subject should try to avoid modifying his respirations voluntarily, and should keep his mind off his rate and mode of breathing. This applies to experiments 2 and 3 also.

2. Take a short record of normal respirations; swing the lever off the drum, and then take a series of very deep respirations for two or three minutes, return the lever to the drum and record the last two or three deep breaths, then hold the breath as long as possible and record the effect as before.

3. Take a short record of normal respirations as a standard. Swing the lever off the drum and do standing running for two to three minutes. Swing the lever back on to the drum, record two or three breaths, hold the breath as long as possible and record the effect.

Run a time-trace. Measure the periods of apnoea and calculate the respiration rates under the various circumstances, and interpret the results.

The Effect of Oxygen Lack.

(123) A stethograph tracing of normal respiration is made, and then, still allowing the stethograph to record, the subject closes his nose and breathes through a soda lime tower into a long wide-bore tube. The observer makes a mark on the trace at this point and watches for any change in the appearance and breathing of the subject. The soda lime absorbs the carbon dioxide of the expired air; nitrogen accumulates in the tube as oxygen does not diffuse in sufficiently quickly to keep up the usual atmospheric concentration.

Changes in Air Breathed.

(124) Breathe on to a cool glass sheet. Expire through a wide-bore tube into lime water; repeat with a *very* weak solution of potassium permanganate. Describe and explain the results.

Tabulate the figures for chest expansion, vital capacity, Flack's test, maximum time of breath-holding, collected from a few of your colleagues and yourself. In one column of your table put your estimate of the physical fitness. Would you say that these figures provide an index of physical fitness?

Artificial Respiration.

(125) It is obviously most important that every one should be able to perform artificial respiration efficiently. The prone-pressure method invented by Schäfer is carried out as follows. Place the patient on his belly, one arm extended directly over-head, the other arm bent at the elbow and with the face turned away from it and resting on the hand or forearm so that the mouth and nose are free for breathing. Kneel straddling the patient's thighs, with your knees near the upper ends of the patient's femora. Place the palms of the hands on the small of the back, with the fingers resting on the ribs, the little fingers just touching the lowest ribs, with the thumbs and fingers in a natural position and the tips of the fingers just out of sight. With arms held straight, swing forward slowly so that the weight of your body is gradually brought to bear on the patient. Your shoulder should be directly over the heel of your hand at the end of the forward swing. Do NOT bend your elbows. This operation should take about two seconds. Now immediately swing backward so as to remove the pressure completely, but do not remove the hands from the patient's back. After two seconds swing forward again.

Repeat deliberately this double movement of compression and release about twelve times per minute; that is, one complete respiration in about five seconds.

When you practise the method on your partner you must impress on him the necessity of letting you take over control of his respiration and of allowing his diaphragm to go slack. Carry out the method, using a watch to keep your rate at exactly twelve per minute. Repeat at fifteen per minute and then at eight per minute. Record the subject's sensations and your own impressions of his reactions. Draw conclusions about the factors governing the rate of application of artificial respiration. ·

ESTIMATION OF METABOLIC RATE

The resting subject breathes through valves into a Douglas bag. The volume of air expired is measured. A sample of the expired air is analysed. The metabolic rate is calculated from the oxygen intake, the caloric value of the oxygen being assessed from the value of the respiratory quotient.

(126) The analysis may be carried out by a simplified form of Haldane apparatus, the operation of which should be studied first. The simplified form is not compensated for alterations of temperature and cannot be expected to give a high degree of accuracy, nevertheless it illustrates very well the principles of gas analysis. Shield the apparatus from draughts and do not breathe on it. The main part is a measuring burette of 10 c.c. capacity with a rubber tube at the lower end connecting with a reservoir. The reservoir and tubing contain mercury, so that if the reservoir is raised and lowered, gas is pushed out or sucked into the burette. At the upper end of the burette is a three-way tap so that the burette may be connected either to the external air or to the horizontal tube which passes to the right to the T tap. Immediately below the T tap is a glass bell immersed in 10 per cent. caustic potash; farther to the right is a glass bell immersed in 10 per cent. pyrogallic acid in saturated caustic potash. Examine both taps very carefully so that they can be used without hesitation in the actual analysis.

Before the apparatus can be used for analysis all CO_2 and O_2 must be cleared out of it. See that the three-way tap at the top of the gas burette communicates with the side tube. Turn the T tap so that the burette is connected to the pyro; adjust the reservoir

to bring the pyro level to the mark just above the glass bell. Then connect the burette to the potash and adjust its level to the mark. Take a reading of the mercury level in the narrow stem of the burette. Now raise and lower the reservoir slowly to bring the gas into contact with the pyro. Repeat several times, connect the burette to the potash bulb, move the air twice forwards and backwards into the potash, connect once more to the pyro and move the air several times back and forth into the pyro. Adjust the pyro level, then the potash level, and read the burette. Repeat this procedure until the burette reading is constant. Do not allow pyro or potash to be sucked up into the T tube. If this happens, the tap will have to be removed at once and cleaned.

An analysis of atmospheric air can now be undertaken.

1. Turn the burette tap so that the burette communicates with the external air.

2. Raise the reservoir until the whole burette and the tube above it are filled with mercury.

3. Lower the reservoir so as to draw in air nearly to the lower end of the burette.

4. Turn the tap to join the burette to the side tube and turn the T tap to communicate with the potash only.

5. Adjust the height of the reservoir till the potash level is at the mark. Read the mercury level in the burette. This is the volume of air drawn in.

6. Raise and lower the reservoir repeatedly.

7. Take readings of the burette when the potash is at the mark. When two consecutive readings are the same all the CO_2 will have been absorbed.

8. Leave the potash at its mark and turn the T tap to connect the burette to the pyro jar.

9. Raise and lower the reservoir slowly, watching the mercury on the upward swing and the pyro on the downward swing.

10. Repeat about twenty times.

11. Bring the pyro to the mark.

12. Turn the T tap so that the burette communicates with the potash.

13. Raise and lower the reservoir several times so as to mix the gas in the potash tube (which contains oxygen) with the gas in the burette.

14. Leave the potash at its mark.

L

15. Push the air over to the pyro, moving it back and forth into the pyro several times.

16. Finally leave the pyro at its mark.

17. Turn the T tap to potash only and bring the potash to the mark.

18. Read off the level of the mercury in the burette. Repeat the whole process and again read the burette when the potash is at its mark. If this reading is the same as the previous, all the oxygen has been absorbed. If not, repeat until two consecutive readings are the same. The apparatus should be left as it is now, full of nitrogen, ready to analyse the expired air.

Collection of the expired air may now be undertaken. Note carefully the way in which the Douglas bag is folded. At the end of each experiment the folds should be in exactly the same place. Lay out the bag flat, open the large tap, and force out all air by folding and compressing it. Close the large tap. Connect the large tube to the expiratory end of the mouthpiece (see Fig., p. 150). See that the clamp on the narrow side tube is closed. The subject adjusts the mouthpiece and puts on a nose clip so that he breathes in and out through the valves, the expired air escaping at the large hole at the tap. After five minutes or so the corrugated connecting tube will have been thoroughly washed through by the subject's expired air. Turn the large tap at the end of an expiration, and at the same time start the stop-watch. At the end of about seven minutes, or before the bag is distended, turn the tap at the end of an expiration and simultaneously stop the watch.

Attach a three-way tap to the upper end of the gas burette by a short rubber tube and connect the narrow side tube of the Douglas bag to it.

1. Turn both three-way taps so that the burette is connected to the external air.

2. Raise the reservoir and fill the burette and the taps with mercury.

3. Turn the three-way tap attached to the side tube of the Douglas bag so that the burette is connected to the bag.

4. Open the screw clip on the bag.

5. Take in a 10 c.c. sample of the expired air by lowering the reservoir.

6. Turn the upper tap and expel the sample to the exterior through it.

7. Repeat this, and then take in a third sample.

8. Turn the burette tap to connect with the potash, adjust the potash level to its mark, read off the volume and proceed with the analysis exactly as with atmospheric air.

Attach the large tube of the Douglas bag to a gas meter. Bring all the indicators to zero—they are sliding fits on their spindles. Turn the large tap—press out the bag slowly so that the main hand of the meter revolves once in not less than six seconds. When the bag is nearly empty fold it up in its original folds and sit on it. When no more flows out turn the large tap and read the volume indicated by the meter, at the same time read the temperature, t, in the meter, and read the barometric pressure, p.

The total volume of expired air, V, will be the meter reading plus the amount used in the analysis, i.e. 30 c.c. Reduce to N.T.P. by the formula—

$$V_{N.T.P.} = V \times \frac{273}{273+t} \times \frac{p-w}{760},$$

where w is the pressure of water vapour at t degrees. The volume of air expired per minute is got by dividing this value by the time of collection (minute volume).

The composition of the atmospheric or inspired air is remarkably constant. It is better to use the known values for atmospheric air rather than those obtained in your analysis, which are subject to error.

$$CO_2 = 0.03\%; \quad O_2 = 20.93\%; \quad N_2 = 79.04\%.$$

Calculate from the observed burette readings the percentage composition of the expired air—CO_2 exp., O_2 exp., N_2 exp. The production of CO_2 can be got by subtracting CO_2 exp. $- CO_2$ insp. since the amount of CO_2 in the inspired air is very low. The amount of oxygen used cannot be got so simply because of the discrepancy between the volume of the inspired and the volume of the expired air. This is due to the fact that the addition to the air of metabolic CO_2 is not usually balanced by an equal subtraction of O_2 from the air. Since the body does not utilise the nitrogen, as much nitrogen enters the lung as leaves it. Since also in the inspired air 79.04 c.c. of N_2 are associated with 20.93 c.c. of O_2 we can calculate by simple proportion the amount of oxygen

taken in (O_2 insp.) if we know the amount of nitrogen breathed out (N_2 exp.). This value is already known.

$$O_2 \text{ insp.} = 20\cdot93 \times \frac{N_2 \text{ exp.}}{79\cdot04}$$

The oxygen used is then O_2 insp. $- O_2$ exp.

$$\text{The R.Q.} = \frac{CO_2 \text{ produced}}{O_2 \text{ used}}, \text{ i.e. } \frac{CO_2 \text{ exp.} - CO_2 \text{ insp.}}{O_2 \text{ insp.} - O_2 \text{ exp.}}$$

The oxygen used per minute is given by multiplying the minute volume of expired air by $\dfrac{O_2 \text{ insp.} - O_2 \text{ exp.}}{100}$

The calorific value of a litre of oxygen at different R.Q.s is given in the text-books. This ranges from 4·7 to 5·05—approximately 5 Calories per litre. The heat output per minute can be obtained by multiplication. The surface area of the subject can be calculated from Du Bois's formula or more easily by Smart's nomogram. The heat can then be expressed as calories per square metre per hour.

Note carefully that you are not to regard the result obtained here as the basal metabolic rate. This is only obtained when the subject is under true basal conditions—viz. has fasted for 12 to 15 hours previous to the determination, is comfortably warm, and has remained in a state of complete physical and mental relaxation for 30 minutes prior to the air collection.

Alveolar Air.

(127) The air breathed out consists of unchanged dead space air followed by alveolar air. By making an extension of the dead space a sample of alveolar air unmixed with atmospheric air can be obtained.

Fix a gas sampling tube in a clamp about three feet above the table on a stand placed in the middle of a large tray. A mercury reservoir (M.R.S.T.) is connected to the lower end of the sampling tube by a length of pressure tubing. Turn the taps so that on raising M.R.S.T. the sampling tube is filled with mercury and the air completely expelled. Close the upper tap and lower M.R.S.T. to table level. When the mercury has all run out of the sampling tube, close the lower tap. Disconnect M.R.S.T.

Sterilise the mouthpiece of the 4-foot long wide tube and attach

the sampling tube to the side tube near the mouthpiece. The subject breathes normally for a little, and then at the end of a normal inspiration puts his mouth to the mouthpiece, expires deeply and quickly, and closes the mouthpiece with the tongue. The upper tap of the sampling tube is turned to admit the air last expelled from the lungs. Close the tap.

Remove the sampling tube and clamp it near the gas-analysis apparatus so that the upper end of the sampling tube can be connected to the upper end of the burette by a short piece of tubing. The gas-analysis apparatus should contain only nitrogen. The tubing from the burette to the sampling tube is cleared of atmospheric air by raising the mercury reservoir of the analysis apparatus (M.R.G.A.) till a drop of mercury escapes (into a small beaker) at the small downward pointing tube at the upper end of the sampling tube. Attach M.R.S.T. to the lower end of the sampling tube once more and raise it a little to fill the lower tap and the small upward pointing tube with mercury. Turn the tap through 180° so that the mercury is pushed up into the sampling tube. Turn the upper tap of the sampling tube and lower M.R.G.A. so as to admit the alveolar air into the burette. Wash the gas backwards and forwards a few times. Shut off the tap on the upper end of the burette and bring the mercury level in M.R.G.A. to the mercury level in the gas burette. Then turn the burette tap to connect to the potash, adjust the potash to the mark and read off the volume in the gas burette. Proceed with the analysis as before (p. 160). If the analysis is satisfactory remove the sampling tube. If it is not, a second sample can be taken from it.

It is usual to analyse a second sample of alveolar air obtained at the end of a normal expiration. The mean of the two samples is taken as the average composition of the subject's alveolar air. Alveolar air is nearly saturated with aqueous vapour at 37° C.; the pressure of the water vapour is about 47 mm. mercury. The tension of CO_2 and O_2 in the alveolar air is calculated thus:

$$\text{Tension of } CO_2 = \frac{\% \ CO_2}{100} \times (\text{barometer reading}-47)$$

$$\text{Tension of } \ \ O_2 = \frac{\% \ O_2}{100} \times (\text{barometer reading}-47)$$

BENEDICT-ROTH APPARATUS

(127a) This apparatus is used clinically where approximate values of the metabolic rate are sufficient. It records graphically only the oxygen used, the CO_2 being absorbed by soda-lime, a granular mixture of $NaOH$ and of $Ca(OH)_2$, which is in a cylinder inside the apparatus. Flutter (duck bill) valves are in circuit so that oxygen is inspired from the spirometer bell and expired air exhaled through the soda-lime. Place soda-lime in its container and run oxygen into the bell. Open valve above mouthpiece to atmospheric air. Place a fresh chart on the drum, wind up the clockwork, place the drum on the spindle, put ink in the pen, and bring the pen against the drum surface just in front of zero time. Make sure that the pen is writing by "pricking" the pen outlet.

The subject lies down supine with mouth just below mouthpiece for about 10 minutes. At the end of the period of rest take the flanged rubber tube out of the antiseptic, wash it in water, insert into subject's mouth so that the flange is between the teeth and cheeks and the rubber blocks gripped by the teeth, and then connect the rubber tube to the apparatus. Allow the subject to rest for 5 more minutes breathing atmospheric air. The subject must be absolutely passive and must pay no attention to the proceedings.

Close the subject's nose with the clip supplied, start the clockwork, and, when the pen point has passed the zero mark, turn the valve to connect the subject to the oxygen in the bell. Turn the valve at the end of an expiratory movement on the part of the subject, and simultaneously start a stop watch. Within the next five minutes count the subject's pulse at the wrist. When the chart is nearly finished, or when the record is approaching the top of the chart, turn the valve to connect the subject to atmospheric air. Do this at the end of an expiratory movement and stop the stop watch. Note the duration of the experiment. Take the temperature of the thermometer at the top of the spirometer bell. Release the subject, swing the pen off the drum, remove the chart.

On the chart put:—Name of subject; age; height in cm.; weight in kg.; pulse rate; respiration rate (count from chart); volume of oxygen used in certain time. The volume of oxygen used may be found by dropping perpendiculars from the beginning and from the end of the record to the ordinate, using the corresponding phase of the respiratory cycle, namely full expiration. The duration of the record is given by the stop watch. Alternatively, a line may be drawn with a ruler along the foot of the respiratory oscillations. If this line is reasonably straight over a period of not less than 10 minutes, drop perpendiculars from the ends of the straight section to the ordinate to find oxygen used and to the abscissa to find time.

Calculate the volume of oxygen used at N.T.P., using temperature of thermometer at top of spirometer bell and barometric pressure of the period, less the pressure of water vapour at the temperature. Assuming no change in metabolism, find the volume of oxygen used at N.T.P. in (a) 1 hour, (b) in 24 hours. Assuming an R.Q. of 0·82, 1 litre of oxygen at N.T.P. has a Calorie value of 4·825. Calculate (a) Calories used in 1 hour, (b) in 24 hours, (c) in 1 hour per sq. metre body surface. (c) is the important reading.

CHAPTER NINE

EXPERIMENTS WITH BLOOD

ENUMERATION OF THE RED AND WHITE CORPUSCLES

(**128**) APPARATUS required: microscope, haemocytometer (counting chamber and pipettes) and diluting fluids.

Each pipette has a narrow stem, graduated in tenths with figures indicating 0·5 and 1·0, which widens into a bulb containing a glass bead. The bulb narrows again, and at this point it is marked either 11 or 101. Beyond this a rubber tube with a glass mouthpiece is attached.

It is most important that these pipettes should be clean and *dry*. Suck up distilled water, blow out into a sink. In the case of the red cell pipette fluid will flow in and out more quickly if the rubber tube and mouthpiece are transferred to the capillary end of the pipette. Repeat several times with water, then with alcohol. Then suck up some ether and allow it to flow out of the pipette by gravity. Now suck air through the pipette to get rid of the ether. Do not blow through the pipette at this stage as the moisture of the breath will prevent drying. The easiest way to get rid of the ether is to attach the rubber tube to a filter pump. When the interior is thoroughly dry, the glass bead will roll about freely without showing any tendency to adhere to the side of the bulb. Transfer the tube and mouthpiece to their correct position on the pipette.

The counting chamber consists of a thick glass slide with a central platform. On each side of the platform but separated by a trough there are two parallel supports for the coverglass, which is thus supported exactly one-tenth of a millimetre above the central platform. Clean the haemocytometer and the special thick coverslip carefully with water and then with alcohol. Dry with a silk handkerchief. Both slide and coverslip must be kept free from any trace of grease or fibres from the polishing cloth.

Sterilise a straight triangular needle either by *gentle* heat or by immersing in alcohol and allowing to dry. Wipe the lobe of your

partner's ear gently with a swab soaked in alcohol. Allow to dry, and then holding the ear gently in the left hand make a quick stab into the fleshy edge of the lobe. Wipe away the first drop. If there is not a free flow of blood do not rub or squeeze the ear; wipe the puncture firmly. If this fails, a fresh puncture should be made. When another drop of reasonable size has collected hold the red cell pipette (it is marked 101 and usually has a red bead) horizontally and apply its tip to the drop of blood and suck up blood to the 0·5 mark or slightly beyond it. Close the mouthpiece by putting the tongue against it. Take the pipette away from the ear and wipe off any blood adhering to the outside. If the blood is beyond the 0·5 mark then touch the tip gently against the back of the hand till the blood is exactly at the mark. Immediately immerse the pipette in the red cell diluting fluid (either Hayem's solution or isotonic saline) and suck up to the 101 mark, rotating the pipette vigorously all the time to mix blood and solution thoroughly. Hayem's solution is $HgCl_2$ 0·05 gm., Na_2SO_4 2·5 gm., NaCl 0·5 gm., water 100 c.c.

Disconnect the rubber tube without squeezing it and close the ends with the finger and the thumb and shake for a minute. Replace the rubber tube and blow out a quarter of the contents so as to remove the pure diluting fluid in the stem.

It is most important to avoid getting clotted blood in the pipette as it is exceedingly difficult to clean. If you think that the blood is likely to clot soon, then blow it out at once and begin all over again.

Moisten the glass bars on either side of the counting chamber with the tip of your finger and press the coverslip firmly down on them so that a series of concentrically arranged rings (Newton's rings) is seen. Bring the tip of the pipette quickly but gently on to the surface of the counting platform where it projects beyond the coverglass, a small amount of the solution will flow under the coverglass. The platform should be covered, but if the fluid flows over the edge of the chamber, or if bubbles appear in it, wash up the slide and try again.

As soon as the cells have settled down (i.e. after two minutes) the count can be made, as the rulings and the cells are then in the same plane. Examine the counting chamber with the low-power objective and a small iris diaphragm. If the distribution of the cells is not uniform, clean the counting chamber and fill it again.

The area covered by the Thoma ruling is a square whose side

is 1 mm.; it is, therefore, 1 sq. mm. in area. The sides of the square are divided into 20 equal parts, each 1/20 mm.; each of the smallest squares is, therefore, 1/400 sq. mm. in area. An additional line, drawn through every fifth square, facilitates counting greatly by marking off the smallest squares into groups of 16. Since the depth of the counting chamber between the coverglass and the rulings is 1/10 mm. the volume over each of the smallest squares is 1/4000 c.mm. Bring the ruling into the centre of the field with the low-power objective, then use the 1/6th objective

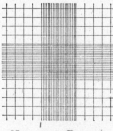

NEUBAUER RULING.

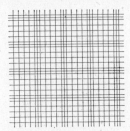

THOMA RULING AND CENTRAL PORTION OF NEUBAUER RULING AS SEEN WITH HIGHER MAGNIFICATION.

with a small iris diaphragm. It should be just possible, if the magnification is correct, to see one group, that is, 16, of the smallest squares in one field. In order to avoid counting the same cells twice in moving from one square to another observe this convention. Count all cells lying on the upper and left lines of any square, omit the cells on the lower and right-hand lines. Count the cells in at least five groups of 16 small squares, i.e. 80 small squares. Since the volume of the fluid on each small square is 1/4000 c.mm. the total volume is 80/4000. As the blood was diluted 1 in 200 by means of the pipette the volume of the blood from which the cells came is really $80/4000 \times 200 = 1/10,000$ c.mm. If n is the number of red cells found in 80 small squares, then $n \times 10,000$ is the number of red cells per c.mm.

(129) The white cell pipette (upper mark 11) is filled in a similar fashion. As a larger quantity of blood is required do not begin to suck up until a fairly large drop of fresh blood is available. Draw blood up to the 0·5 mark and dilute up to the 11 mark with a 1·5 per cent. solution of acetic acid in water, tinted with methyl violet. The acid destroys the red cell envelope so that the red cells

are not seen in the count. The acid also makes the white cells more prominent; the dye colours the nuclei. Shake the pipette and blow out some of the contents.

(Modification of the method of dilution of white cells. The bore of the white cell pipette is large, there is a risk of the fluid running up the rubber tubing or escaping from the pipette, so it is advisable to mix in a watch glass. Immediately the diluting fluid has been drawn to the 11 mark wipe the end of the pipette and blow the diluted blood into a clean dry watch glass and mix thoroughly by sucking up and expelling the fluid several times. Suck it back into the pipette, avoiding bubble formation, to prevent evaporation, and proceed as in the description below. The dilution in this case is 1/22.)

The counting chamber is filled exactly as described for the red cell count, but in this case count all the white cells seen over the whole area of the ruling, i.e. 1 sq. mm. The volume of the fluid over the 1 sq. mm. is 0·1 c.mm., but as the dilution used was 1 in 20 the actual volume of the blood from which the cells came was $0·1 \div 20$. If the number of white cells counted was n the number of cells in 1 c.mm. is $n \times 200$.

Finally, clean up all the apparatus and leave it dry and ready for use.

If the haemocytometer is of the Neubauer type it will be found that its central square is exactly as described for the Thoma pattern, but that the lines are extended so that the total area ruled off is a square of side 3 mm. and area 9 sq. mm. This allows of greater accuracy in counting white cells. Count the total number of cells, say n, in 9 sq. mm., that is, 0·9 c.mm. The dilution being 1 in 20 the number of white cells per c.mm. is given by $n \times 200 \div 9$.

ESTIMATION OF HAEMOGLOBIN

(130) *Haldane's haemoglobinometer.*—Apparatus: a pipette to measure 20 c.mm. of blood, a graduated diluting tube (the volume at the 100 mark is 100×20 c.mm. $= 2$ c.c.), a colour standard.

A small amount of water, up to the mark 10, say, is placed in the dilution tube. As water sometimes causes cloudiness it may be better to use 0·5 per cent. liq. ammon. fort. in distilled water. The pipette is dried in the same manner as the diluting pipettes for cell counting (v. p. 170). A drop of blood is obtained as before (v. p. 170). Suck up to the 20 c.mm. mark, wipe off any blood on the outside, adjust the volume exactly to the mark by tapping on the nail. Blow the blood gently into the water and suck up and

down two or three times to mix thoroughly. Now remove the rubber tube from the pipette and slip the pipette into a rubber tube connected to the coal gas supply; pass the pipette down the tube until it is just above the surface of the diluted blood. Allow some gas to pass and withdraw the pipette slowly to fill the upper part of the tube with gas, then close the end with the thumb and invert several times; finally draw the thumb across the edge so that none of the diluted blood will be lost. Repeat the gas saturation twice, using the same thumb and avoiding loss of fluid. All haemoglobin should now be converted into Hb CO. Add distilled water drop by drop from a pipette. After each addition mix up the contents by (1) inverting the tube, or (2) sucking the fluid up and down a pipette, or (3) stirring with a fine glass rod. The last method will probably result in the smallest loss of fluid, and it avoids frothing. Continue to add water till the tint in the diluting tube is just darker than that of the standard. Compare the tubes against bright diffuse daylight, and also while holding them against a sheet of white paper. Take the reading of the upper level of the fluid in the dilution tube. Continue dilution until the tint is just appreciably paler than the standard. Take the average of this reading and the previous one as the correct reading.

The standard in the Haldane apparatus consists of a 1 per cent. solution of blood which had an oxygen capacity of 18·5 c.c. per 100 c.c. of blood. After dilution it was saturated with CO. This colour standard is stable. 100 per cent. on this scale indicates that the blood has 13·8 g. Hb per 100 c.c. (N.P.L. Standard= 14·8 g. Hb).

(131) *Sahli method*.—The technique is very like that in the Haldane method except that the haemoglobin is converted to acid haematin instead of Hb CO.

Fill the dilution tube to the mark 10, or thereby, with fresh N/10 HCl. Add with the same precautions as before 20 c.mm. of blood. Mix and allow to stand for one minute. Add water drop by drop, and again take the average of the readings when the tint is just lighter and just darker than the standard. The standard may be a tube containing fluid or it may be a solid glass rod. The fluid standard is not so stable and may fade. 100 on this scale means that the blood contains 16 g. Hb per 100 c.c. blood.

(132) *Tallquist Scale*.—This method may be employed where a

rough indication of the haemoglobin content is sufficient. A special piece of absorbent paper is touched against a drop of freshly drawn blood. When the glistening appearance is passed off, the tint is compared with a series of colour standards, making a guess at intermediate values if an exact match is not found.

It is not possible to speak of the normal value of haemoglobin because normality has a very wide range, but the mean value found in healthy subjects is 14·5 gm. Hb per 100 c.c. (males range from 14–17, females from 12–15·5). 14·5 gm. correspond to 105 on the Haldane scale and 91 on the Sahli. There is also a considerable range in the number of red corpuscles in health, but the average, irrespective of sex, is the convenient number 5,000,000 per c.mm. (males average 5,500,000 and females 4,800,000).

Colour Index (C.I.).

(**133**) It has long been customary to calculate the colour index (C.I.) to get an idea of the content of each cell in haemoglobin as compared with the normal.

$$\text{C.I.} = \frac{\text{Haemoglobin (percentage of normal)}}{\text{Red cells (percentage of normal)}} = \frac{100}{100} = 1$$

For convenience it is usual to take 5×10^6 cells per c.mm. as normal. It is also usual to take the percentage of haemoglobin as the percentage on the particular haemoglobinometer used. The value of C.I. will then depend in any one individual on whether the Sahli or Haldane haemoglobinometer is used. The fraction obtained by using the Haldane value of normality 105 instead of a true value of 100 does not introduce any great error. But, strictly speaking, the percentage of normality should be worked out, using the average values 105 Haldane and 91 Sahli before going on to calculate the C.I. E.g. 45 per cent. Haldane and 4×10^6 red cells,

$$\text{C.I.} = \frac{\dfrac{45}{105} \times 100}{80} = 0\cdot54;$$

45 per cent. Sahli and 4×10^6 red cells, $\text{C.I.} = \dfrac{\dfrac{45}{91} \times 100}{80} = 0\cdot62$

Mean Corpuscular Volume (M.C.V.).

(134) Because the C.I. depends partly on cell size and partly on haemoglobin concentration haematologists prefer other measurements which can be calculated when the volume of the red cells is known.

Five c.c. of blood are obtained from a vein and mixed in a small bottle containing 4 mgm. solid potassium oxalate and 6 mgm. solid ammonium oxalate. No cell shrinkage occurs with this amount of salt. The haematocrite tube is filled with the blood and spun till no further reduction in volume of red cells is noted (usually one hour at 2500 revs. per min.). Read off the upper level of the plasma and the upper level of the r.b.c. Calculate the volume of packed cells per 100 c.c. blood (normal value 42 c.c.). If a haematocrite is not available a small graduated conical centrifuge tube can be used with a larger volume of blood. It is worth noting that in such an oxalated blood sample red and white cell counts can very easily be done.

$$\text{M.C.V.} = \frac{\text{Volume of packed red cells per litre of blood}}{\text{Red cells in millions per c.mm.}}$$

=mean volume of a single red cell in cubic microns. Normal range 78–94, average 86 c. μ.

Mean Corpuscular Haemoglobin Concentration (M.C.H.C.).

(135) The material of which the red cells are composed can be regarded as containing or enclosing haemoglobin—normally 42 c.c. of red cells contain 14·5 gm. of haemoglobin. By simple proportion 100 c.c. of red cells would hold 34·5 gm. This is the average M.C.H.C.; the normal range is 32–38 gm. In your own case find the number of gm. haemoglobin carried in 100 c.c. of red cells.

Fragility of the Red Cells.

(136) You are provided with a rack containing nine test-tubes each 3 in. × ½ in. See that they are clean and dry. Also see that the dropping pipette is clean and free from grease; it should be rinsed out several times with the reagent to be measured out. Hold the pipette vertically with the third and fourth fingers, leaving the thumb and first finger free to compress the teat; the drops should be discharged at the rate of one a second, they will then be all of equal size. Go along the tubes first of all with 1 per cent.

NaCl and then distilled water as indicated in the table. Afterwards shake the test-tubes to mix the solutions.

Tube No.	1	2	3	4	5	6	7	8	9
1 per cent. NaCl No. of drops	32	28	24	22	20	18	16	14	12
Water No. of drops	8	12	16	18	20	22	24	26	28
Percentage NaCl	0·8	0·7	0·6	0·55	0·5	0·45	0·4	0·35	0·3

Clean the finger near the nail bed with soap and spirit. Allow it to dry and then prick with a needle sterilised by being heated and then allowed to cool. Let a drop of blood fall into each tube. Invert each tube to mix up the cells. Set aside for one hour before inspecting the result. If there is no haemolysis the red cells will be found at the bottom of the tube with clear saline solution above. If some haemolysis has occurred the saline will be tinged more or less with haemoglobin. If haemolysis is complete then the fluid will be equally coloured throughout and there will be no red cells visible at the bottom of the tube. Record where haemolysis starts (usually 0·45 per cent.) and where it is complete (usually 0·35 per cent.). Finally leave the apparatus clean.

CHAPTER TEN

THE EFFECTS OF EXERCISE

The Effect of Exercise on Pulse and Respiration.

(**137**) WORK in fours: (1) subject, (2) recorder of respiration, (3) recorder of pulse, (4) clerk who enters readings on previously prepared table. *No student who has cardiac disease or who has had rheumatic fever should act as subject.* The table should have three columns for time, pulse rate, and respiration rate. The clerk should enter time at minute intervals for thirty minutes from the beginning of the experiment in the first column, the other two will call out numbers to him which he will enter at once in his table opposite the appropriate time. Meanwhile the subject rests. The two recorders count the pulse by palpation of radial or temporal artery and respiration by observation of chest movements. They count for half a minute, call out numbers, wait for half a minute, and then repeat until the clerk declares that he has a reasonably good base line, say, three very nearly corresponding numbers immediately following one another. In any case do not take these preliminary resting readings for more than five minutes. The subject then runs out of the laboratory and runs up and down the stairs outside the laboratory till he shows quite marked respiratory embarrassment. He returns to his place in the laboratory and sits down again and the observations are repeated until some minutes after the normal has again been reached. The time of going to and coming from exercise is noted in the table by the clerk. One of the others counts the number of times the subject runs up and down the stairs.

Graph the results. Abscissa 1 in. = 5 minutes.

Ordinate 1 in. = 5 respirations, and 1 in. = 20 pulse beats.

The origin (o, o) need not appear on the graph.

The Effect of Exercise on Blood Pressure.

(**138**) Work in fours again: (1) subject, (2) recorder of S.B.P. and D.B.P. by auscultation, (3) recorder of S.B.P. by palpation,

(4) clerk. A table is prepared as before, and the technique described on page 186 followed exactly. Graph the results—abscissa again 1 in.=5 minutes, ordinate 1 in.=20 mm. mercury. Shade in the pulse pressure area.

(**139**) If a quietly running ergometer is available the alteration of B.P. and pulse rate *during* exercise can be investigated. The method to be used is exactly as previously described. The arm carrying the B.P. armlet must be kept still during the B.P. estimations.

Cardiac Tolerance Test.

(**140**) The subject should be seated in a comfortable position with his muscles relaxed for ten minutes (preferably twenty to thirty minutes) before the exercise begins. The observer counts the subject's pulse rate over half-minute periods during the eighth and ninth minutes.

The subject then steps up and down five times on to a box or stool of standard height, viz. 45 cm., keeping time to a metronome set at 96 on the scale (96 beats per min.). Each stepping on and off requires four movements—right foot on, both feet on, right off, left off. Immediately on completion of the exercise the subject sits down and relaxes again.

The observer counts the pulse rate during the first fifteen seconds *immediately* following on the conclusion of the exercise; and again exactly one minute after cessation of exercise (counting for half a minute); and again exactly two minutes after cessation of exercise.

The results should be given in tabular and graphic form and compared with the results obtained by other members of the class.

If another observer is available he should take the blood pressure before the exercise and at fifteen and sixty seconds after the end of the exercise.

Compare the results with those obtained with the much more violent exercise done previously.

CHAPTER ELEVEN

ESTIMATION OF THE COOLING POWER OF THE ENVIRONMENT

(**141**) THE simplest apparatus is the wet and dry bulb thermometer. The dry bulb is an ordinary thermometer. The wet bulb has a wick wrapped round the bulb; the wick dips into a little vessel containing water. The difference between the readings on the two thermometers is a measure of the drying power of the atmosphere. The apparatus also carries a scale and instructions for finding the relative humidity of the air.

(**142**) The Katathermometer is also used. It measures the cooling power of the environment at body temperature (98° F.). Hang the Kata on its stand, immerse the lower end in a mug of water at about 120° F. and bring the alcohol up so that it *half fills* the dilatation at the upper end, quickly remove the mug. (Overheating will break the thermometer.) Dry the bulb with a duster. Start the stop-watch when the alcohol passes the 100° F. mark and stop the watch when it falls to the 95° F. mark. Repeat several times and take the average. The Kata factor engraved on the thermometer gives the millicalories per sq. cm. lost in falling from 100 to 95° F. If the factor is divided by the number of seconds the "dry Kata" reading is obtained—this is a measure of the cooling by conduction convection and radiation.

The experiment can be repeated using a "sock" on the bulb of the thermometer. The presence of the wet sock will alter the rate of cooling because now evaporation as well as radiation convection and conduction are effective. Calculate the "wet Kata" reading.

The human body does not behave by any means exactly like a Katathermometer, but various empirical values have been found in environments suitable for various kinds of work.

	Dry Kata	Wet Kata
Sedentary work	6	18
Light muscular work	8	25
Heavy muscular work	10	30

INDEX

The numbers refer to pages